THE VILLAGE TEACHER

First published in the UK by Head of Zeus in 2021
An Ad Astra book

Originally published in 2020 by CITIC Press Corporation in Beijing, China

9 7 5 3 1 2 4 6 8

A catalogue record for this book is available from the British Library.

ISBN (FTP): 9781800249998
ISBN (E): 9781800240018

Cover art: Zhang Xiaoyu
Editorial consultant: Weihua Liu

Printed in Serbia by Publikum

Head of Zeus Ltd
First Floor East
5–8 Hardwick Street
London EC1R 4RG

WWW.HEADOFZEUS.COM

CIXIN 刘慈欣 LIU

THE VILLAGE TEACHER

A GRAPHIC NOVEL

Writer: Zhang Xiaoyu
Illustrator: Zhang Xiaoyu
Colorist: Pan Zhiming
Cover Art: Zhang Xiaoyu
Translator: S. Qiouyi Lu

ComiChina
HEAD of ZEUS
An Ad Astra Book

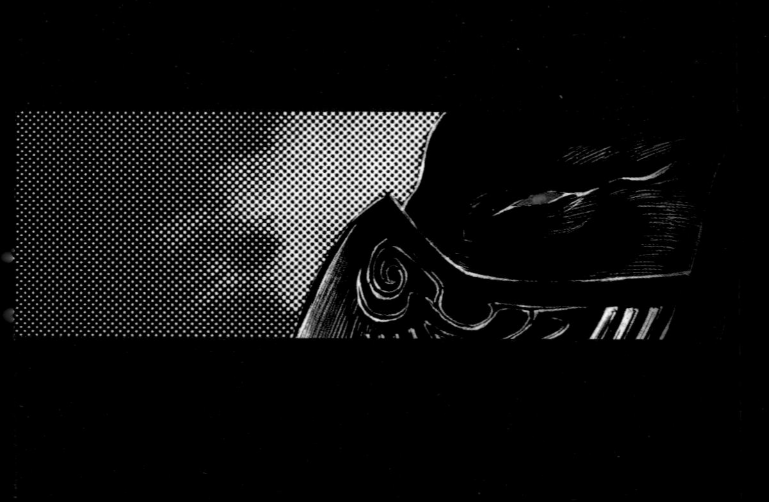

学习天天

DING!
IT'S TIME FOR CLASS.
OPEN YOUR TEXTBOOKS TO CAO CAO'S "BEHOLD THE BLUE-GREEN SEA." LET'S READ IT ALOUD TOGETHER.

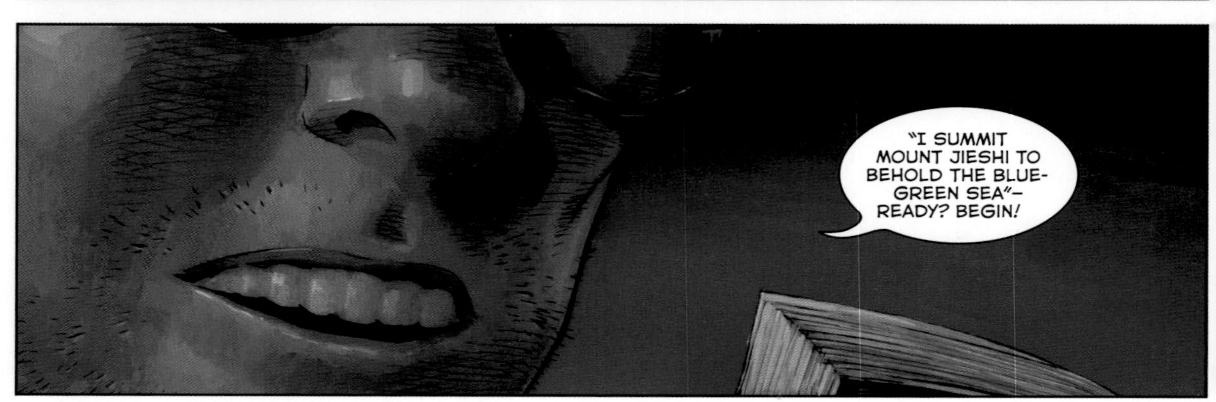
"I SUMMIT MOUNT JIESHI TO BEHOLD THE BLUE-GREEN SEA"– READY? BEGIN!

"I SUMMIT MOUNT JIESHI TO BEHOLD THE BLUE-GREEN SEA."
"HOW QUIETLY THE WAVES RIPPLE; HOW PROUDLY THE PEAKS AND ISLANDS STAND!"

"GRASS GROWS WILD BESIDE A FOREST DEEP."

"THE AUTUMN BREEZE WHISPERS THROUGH LEAVES AS THE SEA SWELLS AND SURGES."

"THE MOON AND SUN CYCLE TOGETHER, AS IF BORN FROM THE WAVES."

"THE MILKY WAY SPARKLES, AS IF UNFOLDING FROM THEIR PATHS."

THE MILKY WAY: CARBON-BASED LIFEFORMS BATTLE SILICON-BASED INVADERS.

THE SILICON EMPIRE FROM BEYOND THE GALAXY HAS MOUNTED AN ALL-OUT ATTACK ON THE CARBONWEALTH. FIVE MILLION GALACTIC WARSHIPS SPAN A FRONT LINE OVER TEN THOUSAND LIGHTYEARS LONG.

SEARULEAN IS THE FIRST TARGET.

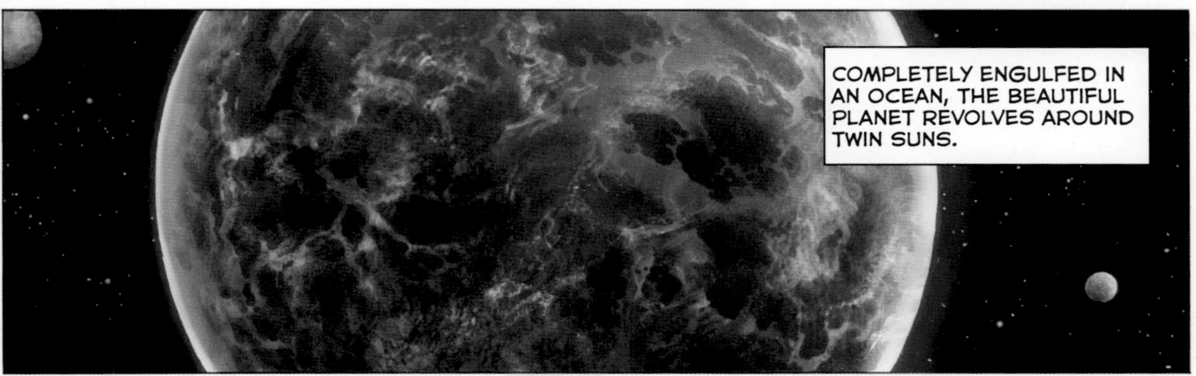
COMPLETELY ENGULFED IN AN OCEAN, THE BEAUTIFUL PLANET REVOLVES AROUND TWIN SUNS.

THE PEOPLE OF SEARULEAN ARE BEAUTIFUL, GENTLE, AND ELEGANT.

SEARULEAN CIVILIZATION IS IDYLLIC, LIKE THE GARDEN OF EDEN.

BUT THE ARRIVAL OF THE SILICON EMPIRE'S WARSHIPS HERALDS ITS END.

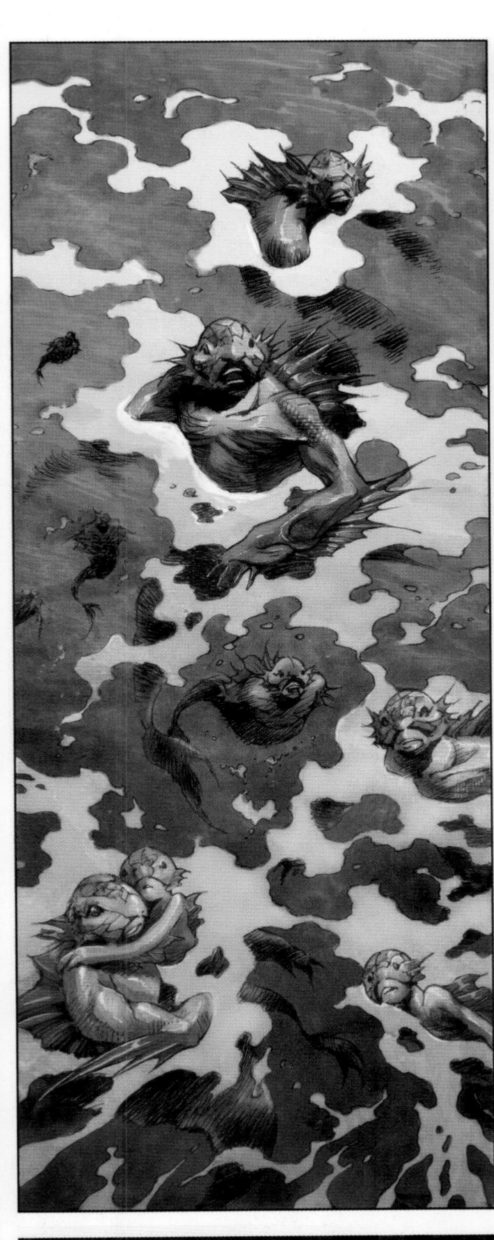

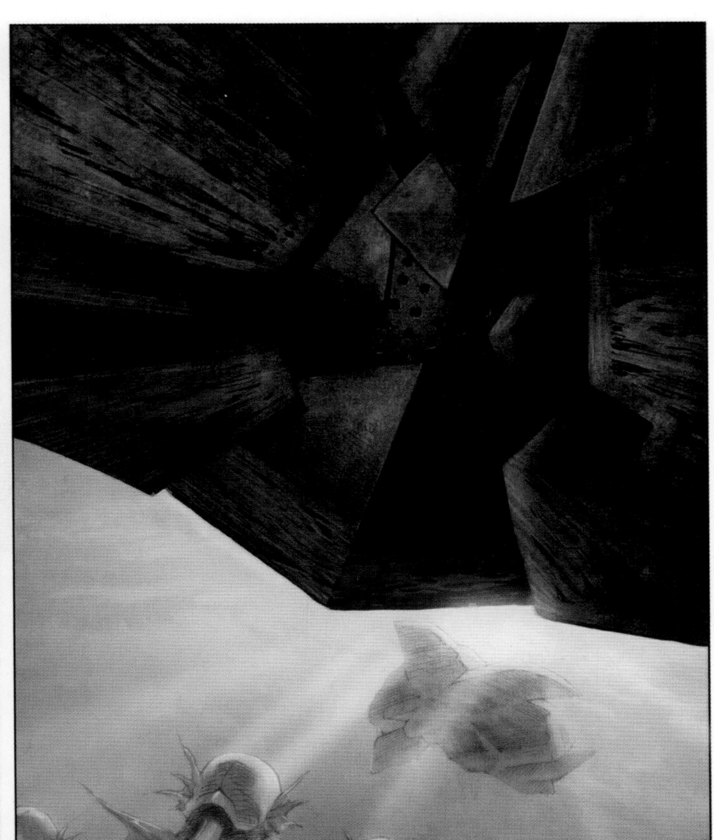

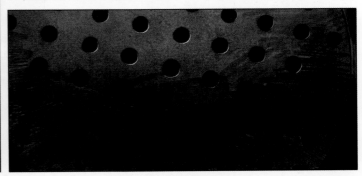

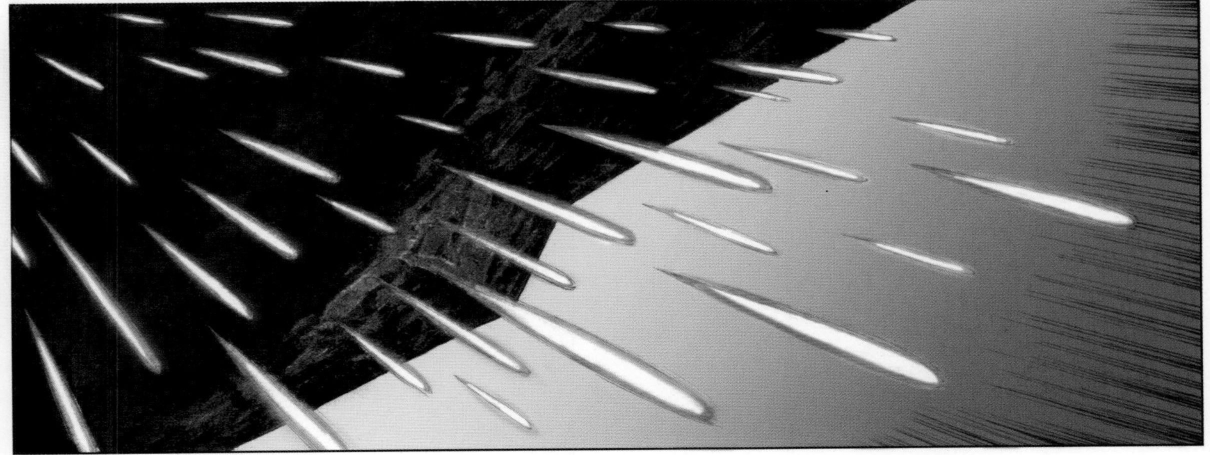

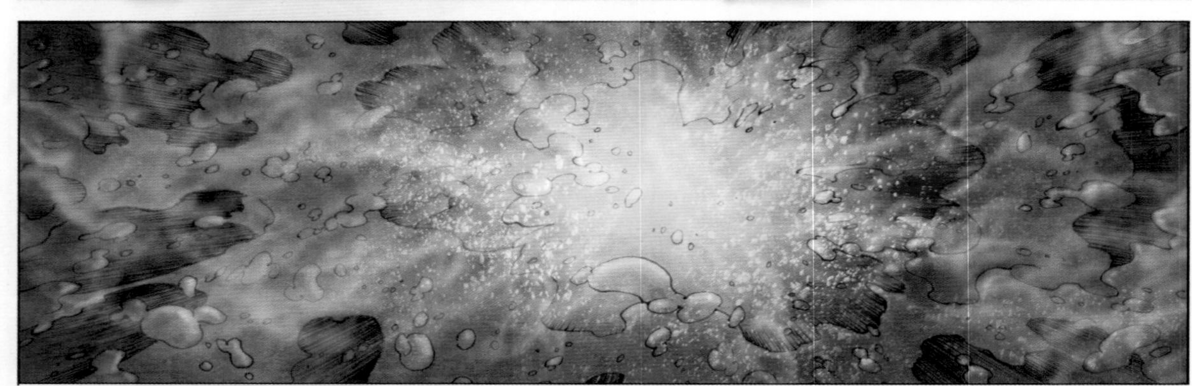

THE SILICON EMPIRE'S DESTROYER AIMS A LASER BEAM AT THE OCEAN.

SOON, THE ENTIRE SURFACE OF THE PLANET BOILS LIKE A CAULDRON.

FIVE BILLION SEARULEANS PERISH IN AGONY.

THE WHOLE OCEAN EVAPORATES.

SEARULEAN IS NOW A HELLISH, ASH-GRAY PLANET WREATHED IN A THICK SHROUD OF STEAM.

THE PLANET'S DESTRUCTION IS A DECLARATION OF WAR ON THE MILKY WAY GALAXY. THE BATTLE BETWEEN THE CARBONWEALTH AND THE SILICON EMPIRE HAS BEGUN.
NO ONE COULD HAVE PREDICTED THAT THE WAR WOULD GO ON FOR 20,000 MILKY WAY YEARS.

MILKY WAY GALAXY, BATTLE OF SPIRAL ARM TWO

COMMANDER! THE FLEET COLLIDED WITH THE ENEMY'S ANTIMATTER BARRIER. THE DAMAGE IS HEAVY–WHAT'S OUR NEXT MOVE? I REPEAT, WHAT'S OUR NEXT MOVE?

CONTINUE THE ATTACK.

WE'LL BE DESTROYED!

ONLY BY SACRIFICING 300,000 WARSHIPS CAN WE CLEAR A PATH THROUGH THE ANTIMATTER CLOUD FOR THE SECOND LINE OF ATTACK...
AND THE CARBONWEALTH'S VICTORY!

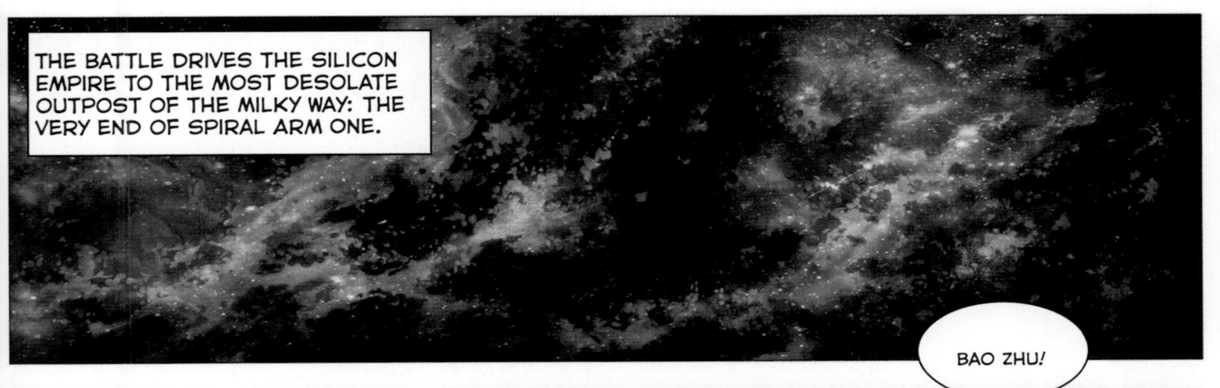
THE BATTLE DRIVES THE SILICON EMPIRE TO THE MOST DESOLATE OUTPOST OF THE MILKY WAY: THE VERY END OF SPIRAL ARM ONE.

BAO ZHU!
BAO ZHU!

狂人日记
作者 鲁迅
ARE YOU SLEEPING IN CLASS?

NO, SIR. I WASN'T SLEEPING.

DO YOU FEEL ILL? YOU HAVE TO TELL ME IF YOU FEEL UNWELL.
狂人日记

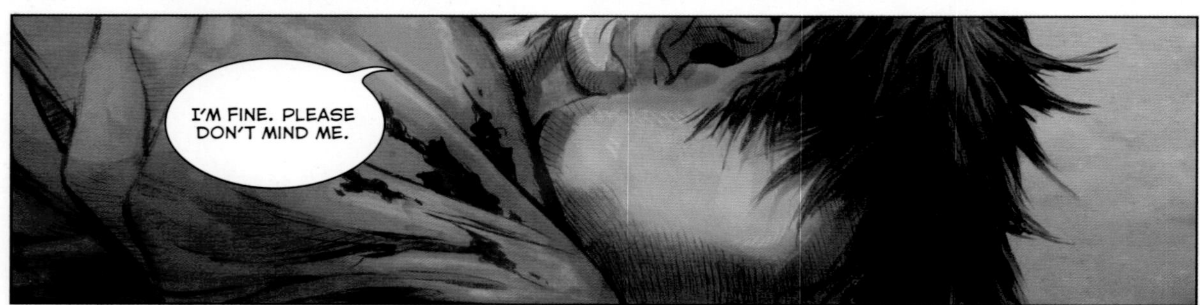
I'M FINE. PLEASE DON'T MIND ME.

BAO ZHU, LOOK UP.

OH...

狂人日记

WHAT THE FUCK, WHY AM *I* THE LAST ONE TO TRY IT OUT? YOU THINK I'M A GOD-DAMN FOOL?

WATCH YOUR LANGUAGE, DU LAO ER. WE'RE STILL TALKING THINGS OVER, AREN'T WE?
YOU AND YOUR IDEAS— *I'M* NOT GONNA TOUCH IT!

CITY PEOPLE SENDING THIS CRAP OVER—WHAT A JOKE. WHAT CAN THIS TINY SHITHOLE EVEN PRODUCE? CAN WE USE IT TO MAKE GOLD?
ALL YOU PHILOSOPHERS CAN GET IN LINE BEHIND ME. I WON'T BE THE LAST TO HAVE ONE!
IT LOOKS COMPLICATED, BUT IT'S USE-LESS. HEH.
COME ON, THEY SENT THIS MINI-TRACTOR TO HELP REDUCE POVERTY. THEY'RE EASY TO USE. YOU ALL SHOULD REALLY GIVE THIS SOME PROPER CONSIDERATION.
IF IT WERE *ACTUALLY* GOOD FOR US, THEY'D GIVE ONE TO EVERY HOME. NO ONE WOULD NEED TO FIGHT OVER THEM.

MY CRAPPY PLOT OF LAND IS EMBROIDERED WITH CROPS NOW! IF I CAN GROW ENOUGH FOR MY FAMILY FOR A YEAR, THAT'D BE INCREDIBLE.

WITH THIS YEAR'S DROUGHT, WE CAN'T EVEN GET THE COST OF THE SEEDS BACK! NOW WE HAVE TO MAINTAIN THIS PILE OF SCRAP?
DIESEL IS ALREADY OVER TWO BUCKS A LITER. BAH!

CHEEP CHEEP!
STOP BICKERING. SO HOW ARE WE GONNA SPLIT IT UP? CHIEF, WHAT'S OUR PLAN?
I DON'T HAVE TIME FOR ALL THIS. I'M NOT IN THE MOOD TO ENTERTAIN YOU ALL—I'M LEAVING!
THEN... DU LAO ER, YOU'RE THE LOUDEST. WHAT DO YOU THINK?
HMPH! WHAT'S SO DIFFICULT? DON'T YOU WANT TO SPLIT IT UP? THEN DO IT!

TO EVERYONE'S SATISFACTION, THE AXLES WENT TO YONG WANG. DA LIU TOOK THE BELT PULLEYS AND OIL TANKS. THE WHEELS WENT TO DONG SHENG AND DU LAO ER.

♫ HEY, YEAH, YEE-ER YEAH! ♫

HEY!
HUH?

ARE YOU THE ONE...
WHO LEFT THESE MARKS ON BAO ZHU?

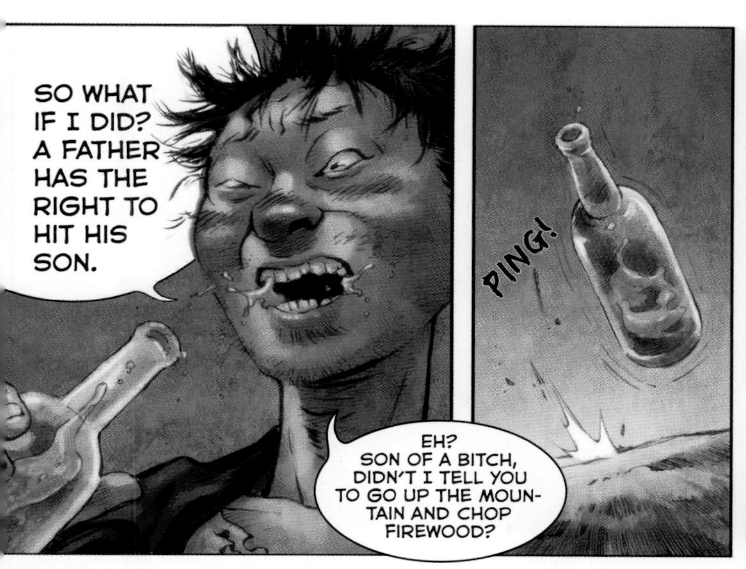
SO WHAT IF I DID? A FATHER HAS THE RIGHT TO HIT HIS SON.
PING!
EH? SON OF A BITCH, DIDN'T I TELL YOU TO GO UP THE MOUN-TAIN AND CHOP FIREWOOD?

SNAP!
YOU RAN OFF TO SCHOOL BEHIND MY BACK?

AND THEN YOU SNITCHED ON YOUR DAD? INGRATE!
STOP! HAVE YOU GONE MAD?!
I'M GOING TO BEAT YOU TO DEATH, YOU LITTLE BASTARD.

JUST TRY AND HIDE, YOU SON OF A BITCH!

POW!

YOU...
MR. L-LI, I D-D-D-D-DIDN'T...

BASTARD!

THUD!

YOU LIKE HITTING PEOPLE? LET ME HELP YOU OUT!

HAVE MERCY!

THAT LITTLE FAGGOT RAN OFF WITH EVERY CENT! THE ONLY THINGS LEFT AT HOME ARE THE ROOF AND A BED!
I JUST LIKE TO DRINK AND GAMBLE A LITTLE. DO I DESERVE TO DIE?

IF BAO ZHU GOES TO SCHOOL, WHO WILL TAKE CARE OF EVERYTHING AT HOME? I CAN'T DO IT ALL MYSELF!

YOU CAN'T DO IT ALL YOURSELF, SO YOU BEAT HIM? ARE YOU REALLY HIS FATHER?!
FROM NOW ON, BAO ZHU WILL STAY AT SCHOOL. TUITION, ROOM AND BOARD– I'LL PAY FOR IT ALL.

BAO ZHU, LET'S GO!

BASTARD! YOU FUCKING BASTARD...

ALL SCHOOL CHILDREN STRUGGLE.

GUO CUIHUA WAS EVEN WORSE OFF THAN BAO ZHU. I FOUGHT FOR HER TO BOARD AT SCHOOL, TOO. SHE'S FROM THE VILLAGE AND WOULDN'T HAVE NEEDED TO LIVE THERE.
BUT HER MOTHER IS A LUNATIC WHO STABS PEOPLE BY DAY AND SETS HOUSES ON FIRE BY NIGHT.

EVERYONE ELSE IS FROM OUT OF TOWN. THE NEXT CLOSEST VILLAGE IS 5 KM AWAY VIA A MOUNTAIN PATH. THEY HAVE NO CHOICE BUT TO BOARD AT SCHOOL.

THEY STAY FOR THE ENTIRE SEMESTER. THEY BRING NOT ONLY THEIR OWN BEDDING, BUT ALSO BAGS OF RICE, FLOUR, WILD VEGETABLES PLUCKED FROM MOUNTAINS, POTATOES... BARELY ENOUGH TO LAST THE FOUR MONTHS.

SIZZLE SIZZLE

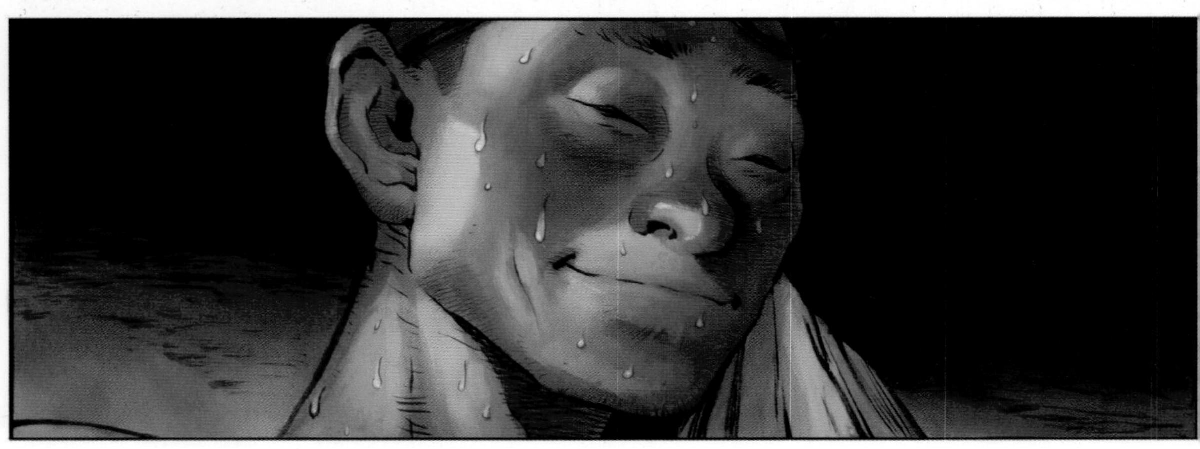

SIR, THE POWER'S GONE OUT AGAIN!
MM.

STRIKE!

OKAY. LET'S CONTINUE. NOW, JUPITER...
太阳系 八大行星
太阳

JUPITER IS THE LARGEST OF THE EIGHT PLANETS IN OUR SOLAR SYSTEM. JUPITER IS A GAS GIANT COMPRISED MOSTLY OF HYDROGEN AND HELIUM, BUT IT DOESN'T HAVE THE OXYGEN WE BREATHE...
火星
木星
土星

TEACHER!

ISN'T THERE ANYONE ELSE IN THE UNIVERSE LIKE US?

THE UNIVERSE IS VERY BIG. I'M SURE LIFE EXISTS ELSE-WHERE, TOO.
水星
金星

WHERE? WHERE?

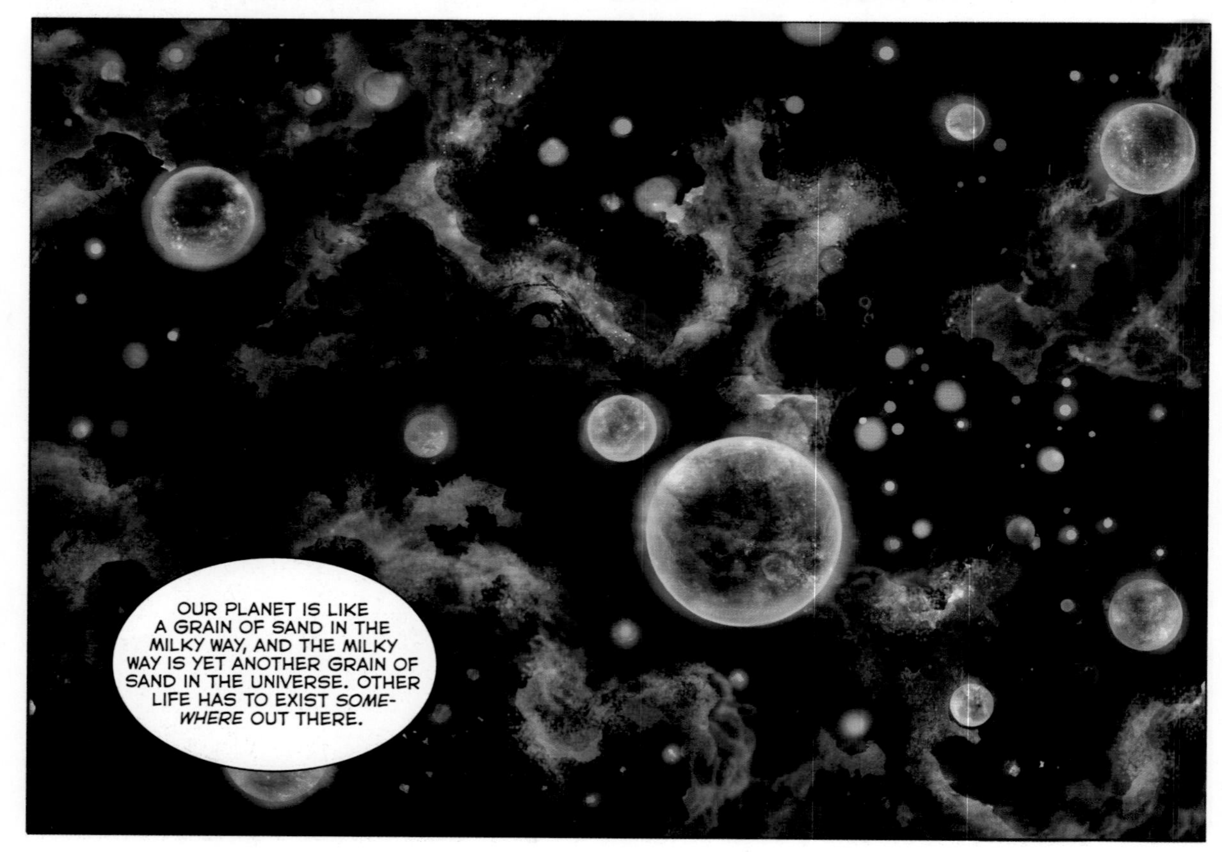
OUR PLANET IS LIKE A GRAIN OF SAND IN THE MILKY WAY, AND THE MILKY WAY IS YET ANOTHER GRAIN OF SAND IN THE UNIVERSE. OTHER LIFE HAS TO EXIST *SOME-WHERE* OUT THERE.

HAVE THEY VISITED US BEFORE? DO THEY KNOW ABOUT US?
HMM... I'M SURE THEY'VE VISITED BEFORE. THEY MUST KNOW WE EXIST.

BUT THE UNIVERSE IS SO BIG. HOW DID THEY GET HERE? ON AIRPLANES?

SQUEAK

SWISH

THEY RODE ON THIS AND WATCHED US FROM THE SKY.

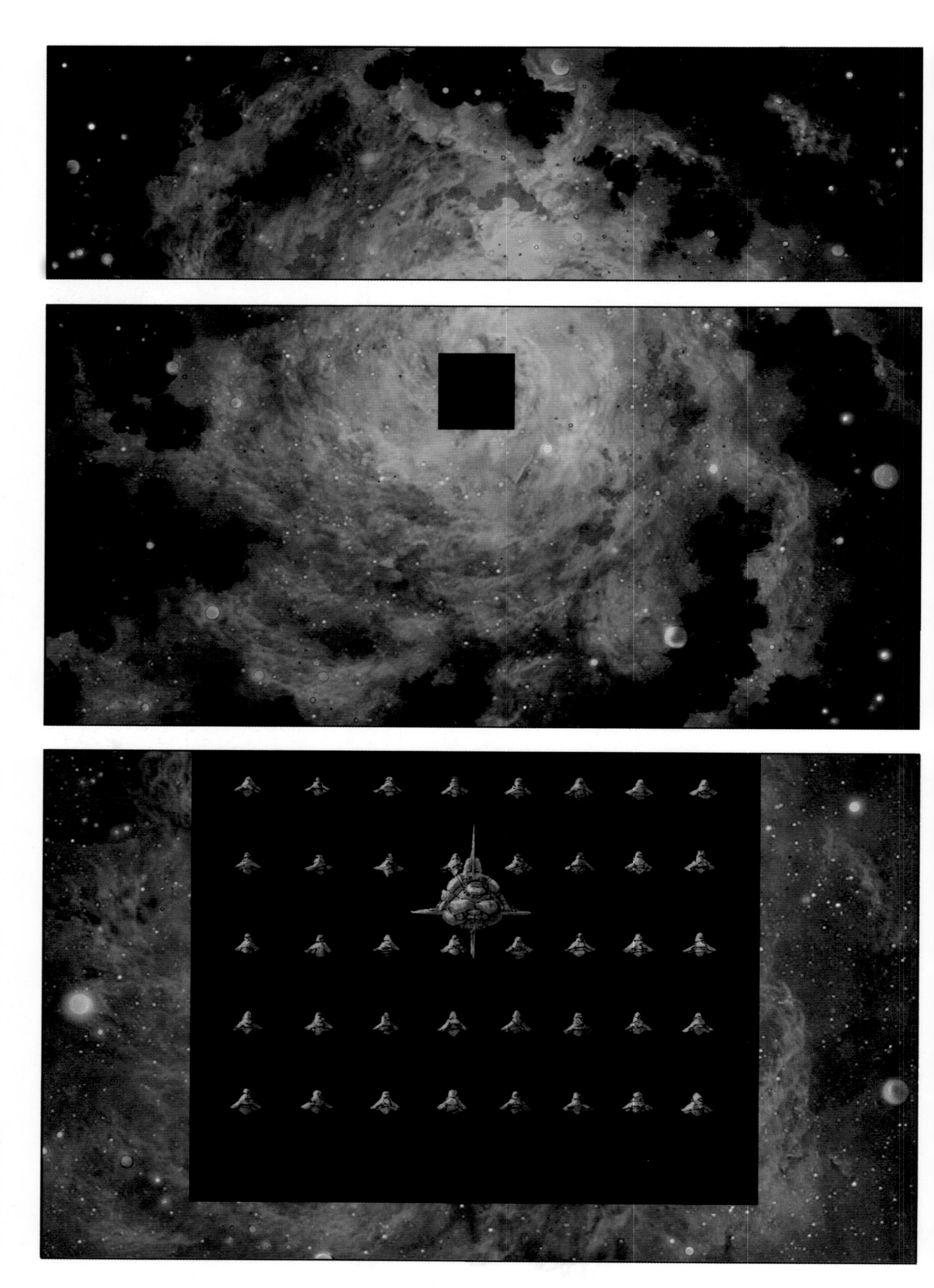

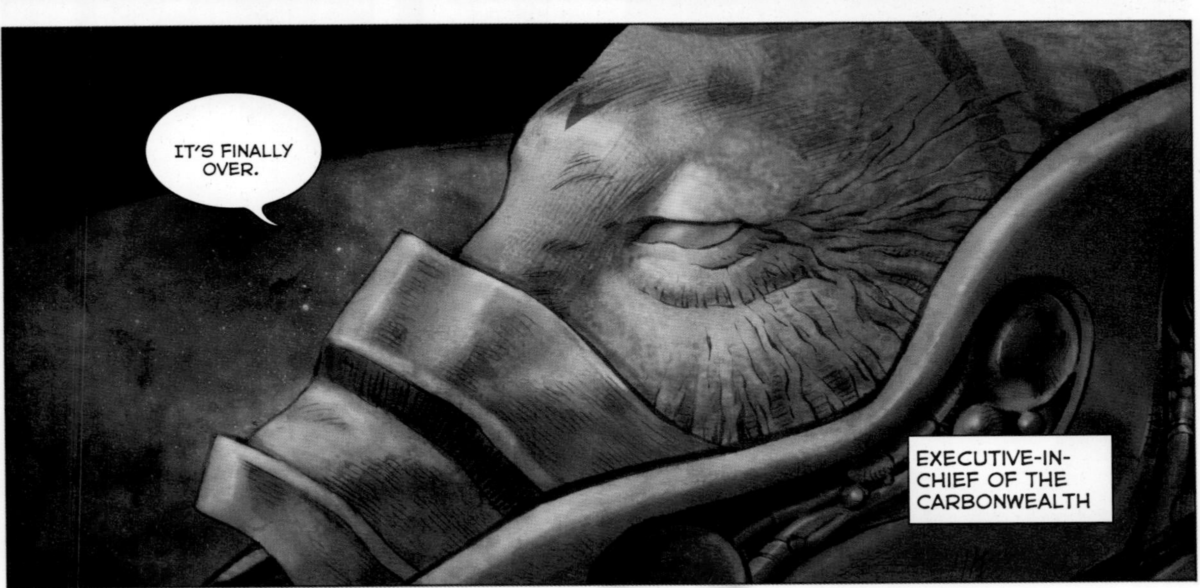
IT'S FINALLY OVER.
EXECUTIVE-IN-CHIEF OF THE CARBONWEALTH

YES, IT'S OVER. WARS LAST FOR FAR, FAR TOO LONG...
SO LONG THAT WE FORGET HOW THEY BEGAN.

THE CARBONWEALTH INTERSTELLAR NAVY HAS COMPLETED ITS FIRST LEAP THROUGH SPACE-TIME.

COMMANDER-IN-CHIEF OF THE CARBONWEALTH NAVY
ONCE WE COMPLETE THIS MISSION, WE'LL HAVE UNDERMINED ALL THEIR TACTICS...

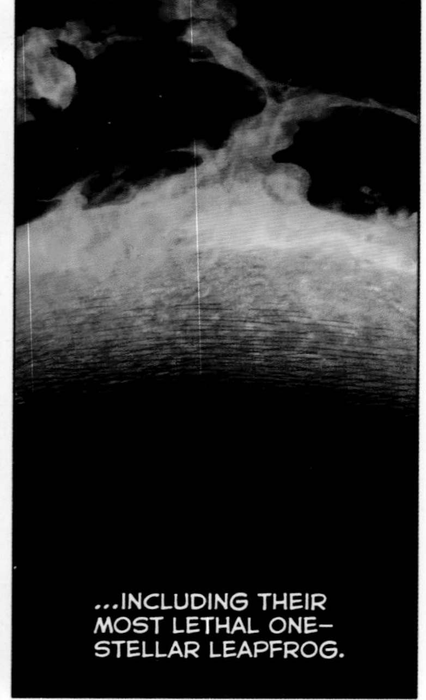
...INCLUDING THEIR MOST LETHAL ONE— STELLAR LEAPFROG.

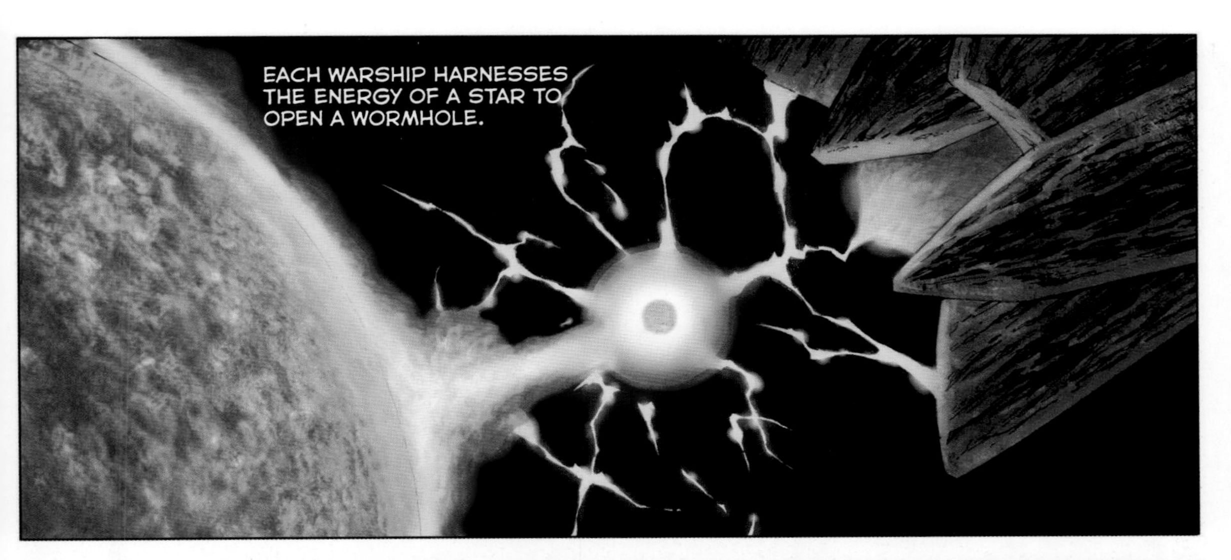
EACH WARSHIP HARNESSES THE ENERGY OF A STAR TO OPEN A WORMHOLE.

THEY THEN LEAP THROUGH SPACE-TIME TO ARRIVE AT ANOTHER STAR.
THEN, THEY USE THE ENERGY OF THAT STAR TO OPEN ANOTHER WORMHOLE...

WHEN THEY ARRIVE AT THEIR DESTINATION, EACH WARSHIP RELEASES FLEETS OF SMALLER BATTLESHIPS. THE SILICON EMPIRE CAN ZIP THROUGH TEN THOUSAND LIGHT YEARS AT A TIME.

ESTEEMED COMMANDER-IN-CHIEF AND INTERSTELLAR NAVY SENATE, WE ARE ABOUT TO ACCOMPLISH THE LAST MISSION IN THIS WAR...
CREATING AN ISOLATION ZONE FIVE HUNDRED LIGHT YEARS WIDE, RIGHT IN THE MIDDLE OF SPIRAL ARM ONE.

WE HAVE NO CHOICE BUT TO DESTROY MOST OF THE STARS WITHIN THE ISOLATION ZONE TO PREVENT THE ENEMY FROM USING THEM. EVEN IF THEY PENETRATE INTO THE ISOLATION ZONE, THEY'D HAVE TO TRAVEL BELOW THE SPEED OF LIGHT TO REACH THE CENTER OF THE MILKY WAY, WHICH IS FIVE HUNDRED LIGHT YEARS AWAY.

THE SILICON EMPIRE WILL BE CONFINED TO THE OUTER REACHES OF SPIRAL ARM ONE. THEY WILL NEVER THREATEN US AGAIN.

I'VE BROUGHT A REQUEST FROM THE CARBONWEALTH PARLIAMENT. WE IMPLORE YOU TO CHECK EACH STAR SYSTEM FOR SIGNS OF LIFE BEFORE DEMOLITION.

DISTINGUISHED MEMBER OF THE SENATE, WE MUST QUICKLY ESTAB-LISH A WIDE ENOUGH DISTANCE BETWEEN US AND THE BRUTAL AND MILITANT SILICON EMPIRE. WE CAN'T SPARE THE TIME TO SCREEN EVERY LAST STAR FOR LIFE UNDER THESE CIRCUMSTANCES.

WE CAN ONLY CHECK FOR SIGNS OF CIVILIZATION. SOME PLANETS WITH LOW-LEVEL LIFE FORMS WILL HAVE TO BE SACRIFICED TO SAVE COUNTLESS MORE LIVES IN THE MILKY WAY.

THE PARLIAMENT UNDERSTANDS. THIS IS A REQUEST, NOT A DEMAND. BUT ALL STAR SYSTEMS WITH LEVEL 3C CIVILIZATIONS AND ABOVE MUST BE SAFEGUARDED.

WITHOUT A DOUBT. WE'LL CONDUCT STRINGENT CHECKS ON EACH PLANET.

YOU'RE ALL OVERTHINKING THIS. SPIRAL ARM ONE IS THE MOST DESOLATE AND REMOTE PART OF THE GALAXY...

THERE WON'T BE ANY LEVEL 3C CIVILIZATIONS.

I'LL FIGHT ANYONE WHO TOUCHES MY SCHOOL!

WHAT KIND OF BULLSHIT ARE YOU SPOUTING, LI? US, SCARED OF *YOU*? FUCKIN' CRAZY!

WE'RE JUST TAKING A FEW BEAMS FROM THE LIVING QUARTERS! THE TEMPLE AT THE TOWN ENTRANCE NEEDS TO BE REPAIRED. WHAT ARE YOU BEING SO STUBBORN ABOUT?!

I HAVE TO AGREE TO ANYTHING THAT HAPPENS TO THE SCHOOL!

PTUI!
THIS CRAPPY SCHOOL PISSES ME OFF!

SURE, YOU'RE THE ONE WHO APPLIED FOR FUNDING FROM THE BUREAU OF EDUCATION. BUT ALL WE DID WAS TAKE SOME SPARE CHANGE.
WE CAN'T INVITE SOME PERFORMERS TO PUT ON A COUPLE OF SHOWS FOR EVERY-ONE TO ENJOY?
GODDAMMIT, THE SET WAS ALREADY BUILT! YOU THINK YOU'RE SO GREAT, YOU SON OF A BITCH? DRAGGING IN THE ASSISTANT COMMISSIONER TO MAKE US COUGH UP THE MONEY— AND THEN YOU EVEN HAD US WRITE SOMETHING SELF-FLAGELLATING! WE HAD TO TAKE DOWN THE SET, AND EVERYONE LOST INTER-EST. HOW CAN YOU BE SO CRUEL?

YOU'RE THE CRUEL ONES! WHY HAS OUR VILLAGE BEEN POOR FOR GENERATION AFTER GENERATION? WE'RE UNEDUCATED! OUR MINDS ARE WEAK! FOR THE VILLAGE TO CHANGE, WE HAVE TO BEGIN WITH THE CHILDREN!
YOU ALL HAVE IT GOOD. YOU'RE ONLY CONCERNED WITH WATCHING SHOWS AND REPAIRING THE TEMPLE. WHAT HAS YOUR SACRED LORD LAOZI DONE FOR YOU, HUH?

CAN A ROOF STAY UP WITHOUT RAFTERS? HOW ARE THE KIDS GOING TO LIVE HERE WITHOUT A ROOF OVER THEIR HEADS?

THEY CAN SLEEP IN THE CLASSROOM.

THE CLASSROOM IS DRAFTY. ONCE WINTER COMES, THEY'LL FREEZE TO DEATH.

THEY'RE ALL OUT-OF-TOWN BRATS. LIKE I GIVE A SHIT IF THEY FREEZE TO DEATH!
PTUI!

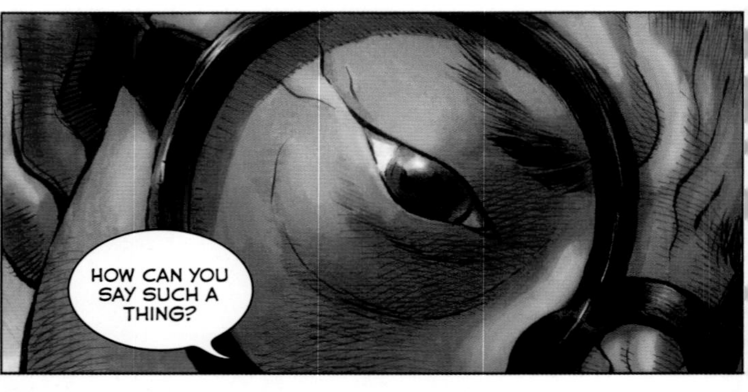
HOW CAN YOU SAY SUCH A THING?

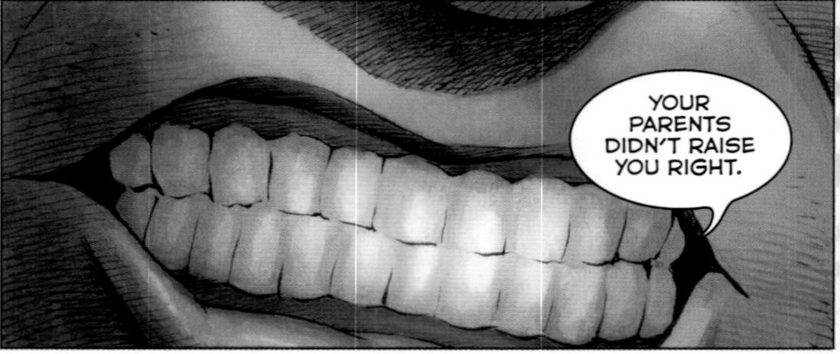
YOUR PARENTS DIDN'T RAISE YOU RIGHT.

YEAH, MOTHER-FUCKER?
COME ON. I'LL BEAT YOUR ASS, YOU BASTARD!

-SOB- HANG IN THERE, MR. LI...
HOW MUCH LONGER UNTIL WE GET TO THE HOSPITAL?
HUFF PUFF
HUFF PUFF
WE'LL GET THERE... BEFORE DARK...

HANG IN THERE, SIR! WE'RE ALMOST AT THE HOSPITAL!

BAO ZHU... MY GLASSES...

I HAVE THEM, BUT ONLY THE FRAMES. THE LENSES ARE GONE...

THAT'S FINE. THEY DIDN'T HAVE ANY TO BEGIN WITH.
HUH?
HELP ME PUT ON THE FRAMES...

SOB
HOW COULD THEY BEAT YOU UP LIKE THIS? AREN'T WE ALL ONE VILLAGE?

YES, INDEED... ALL ONE VILLAGE. THIS IS MY HOME, TOO.
I SPENT MY CHILDHOOD HERE.

WHEN... DID I BECOME DIFFERENT...
FROM THE OTHER VILLAGERS...?

TWENTY-FOUR YEARS AGO,
MY PARENTS PASSED AWAY.

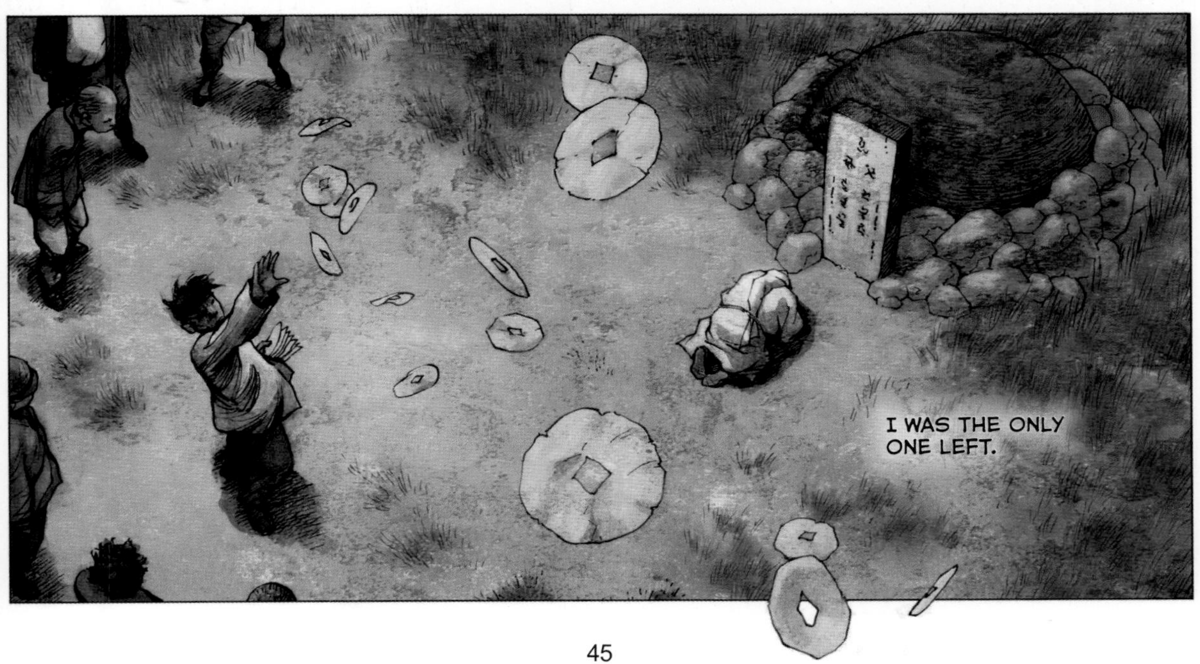
I WAS THE ONLY
ONE LEFT.

李金全

BUT I DIDN'T SUFFER.

I DIDN'T EVEN GRIEVE LONG, BECAUSE...

A TEACHER ARRIVED.

希望学校
HE TOOK ME TO A SIMPLE SCHOOLHOUSE, WHICH BECAME MY HOME.

I WASN'T JUST HOUSED AND FED.

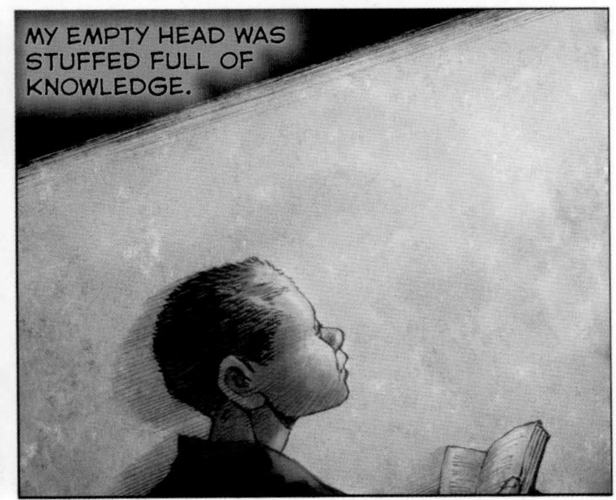
MY EMPTY HEAD WAS STUFFED FULL OF KNOWLEDGE.

THE DAYS PASSED, ONE AFTER ANOTHER, ALWAYS IN POVERTY...

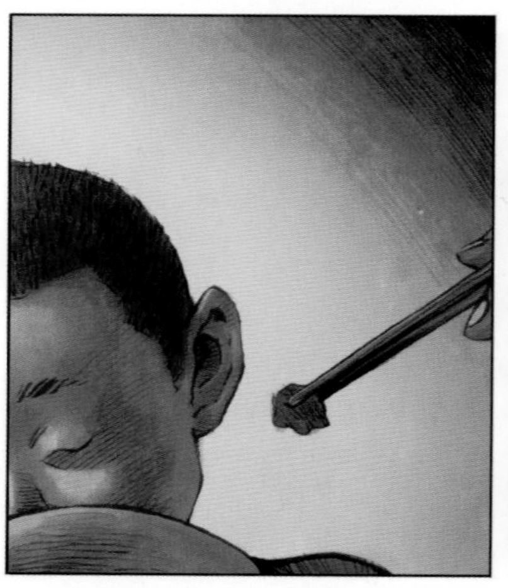

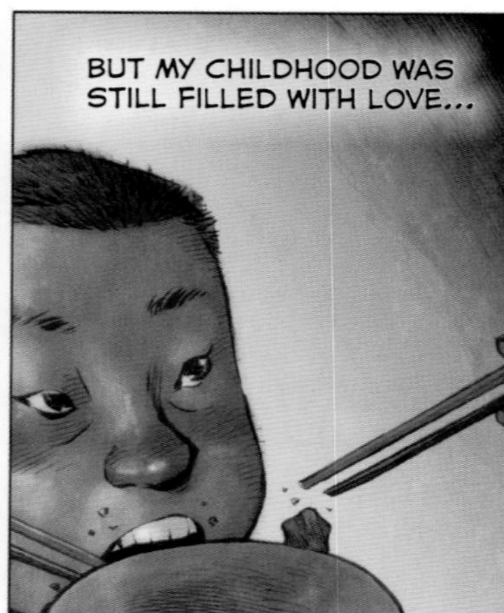
BUT MY CHILDHOOD WAS STILL FILLED WITH LOVE...

UNTIL THAT WINTER.
COME SPEND NEW YEAR WITH ME. I CAN'T HAVE YOU FREEZING BY YOURSELF AT SCHOOL OVER THE HOLIDAYS.

HIS HOME WAS FAR AWAY. WE WALKED FOR A LONG TIME THROUGH THE SNOW-COVERED MOUNTAINS...
SEE, THAT'S MY VILLAGE. WE'RE ALMOST THERE!
YEAH!

TEACHER! TEACHER!

LOOK!

AWOOOOO

HUH?
RUN TO THE VILLAGE! HURRY, CALL THE VILLAGERS FOR HELP!

HURRY!

I WAS SCARED SHITLESS. I DIDN'T KNOW IF THE WOLVES WOULD CHASE ME, OR IF I WOULD RUN INTO MORE.

BANG
BANG
BANG!

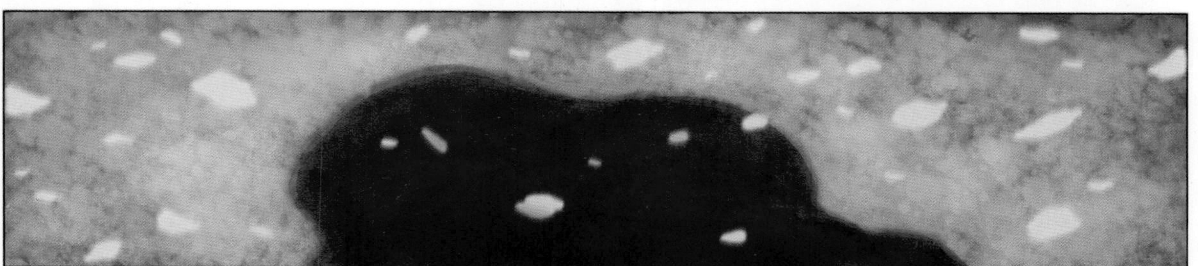

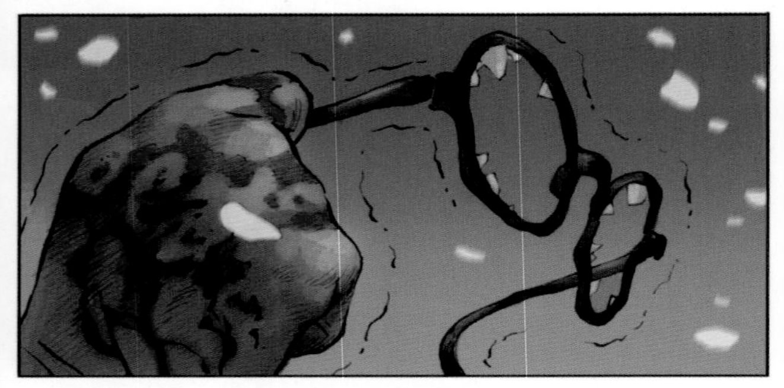

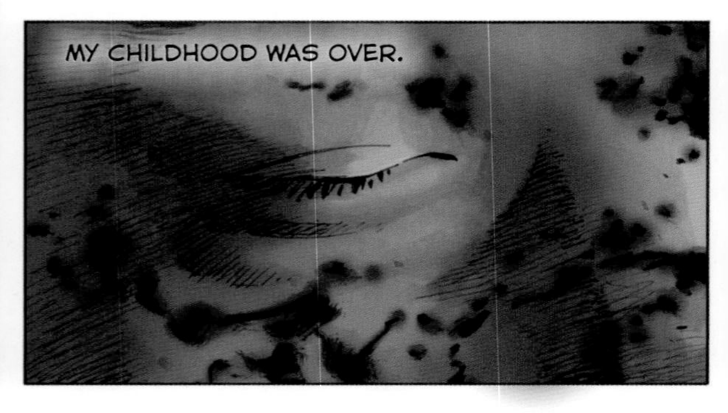
MY CHILDHOOD WAS OVER.

YOUR CHEEK BONE AND STERNUM ARE BROKEN; THE FOURTH AND SIXTH RIBS ARE FRACTURED; AND THERE'S A LOT OF SOFT TISSUE DAMAGE ACROSS THE ARMS, ABDOMEN, AND LOWER BACK.
民医院

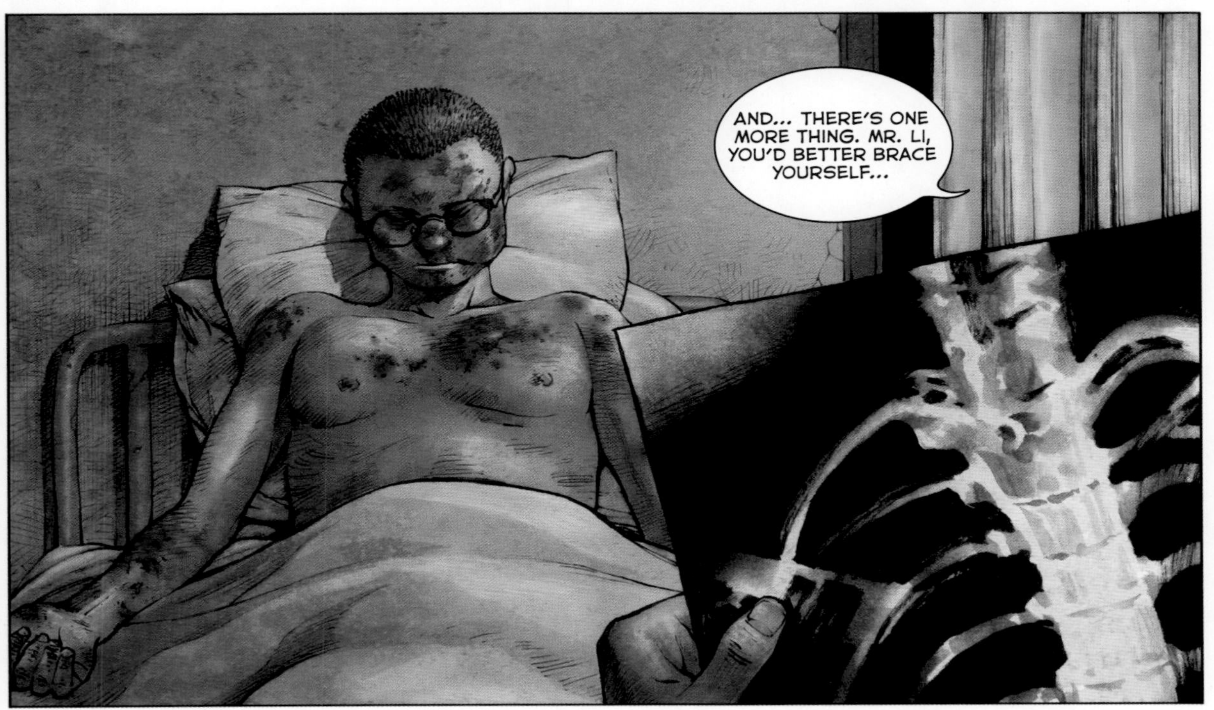
AND... THERE'S ONE MORE THING. MR. LI, YOU'D BETTER BRACE YOURSELF...

WHILE WE WERE EXAMINING YOUR WOUNDS, WE DISCOVERED A TUMOR ON YOUR ESOPHAGUS.

YOU'LL HAVE TO GO TO THE PROVINCIAL HOSPITAL TO CONFIRM THE DIAGNOSIS.DON'T PUT IT OFF.

THERE'S SOME GOOD NEWS, THOUGH.
科主任办公室
Room For Section

WE DETECTED THE MASS EARLY, AND IT HASN'T SPREAD YET.
IF THE SURGERY IS SUCCESSFUL, YOU'LL BE CURED.

ESOPHAGEAL CANCER HAS THE HIGHEST RECOVERY RATE. KEEP A POSITIVE ATTITUDE.
MM.

SIR... HOW MUCH WOULD THE SURGERY COST?

YOU'RE CONSIDERED A RESIDENT OF AN IMPOVERISHED AREA. YOU CAN STAY IN THE LOW-INCOME FACILITIES.
THERE ARE WAIVERS FOR OTHER EXPENSES. THE COSTS WILL BE MINIMAL IN THE END—NO MORE THAN ¥20,000 OR SO.

THE MOST IMPORTANT THINGS ARE TO HAVE AN OPTIMISTIC ATTITUDE AND TO COOPERATE.
DOCTOR...

IF I DON'T DO THE SURGERY, HOW LONG WILL I HAVE TO LIVE?

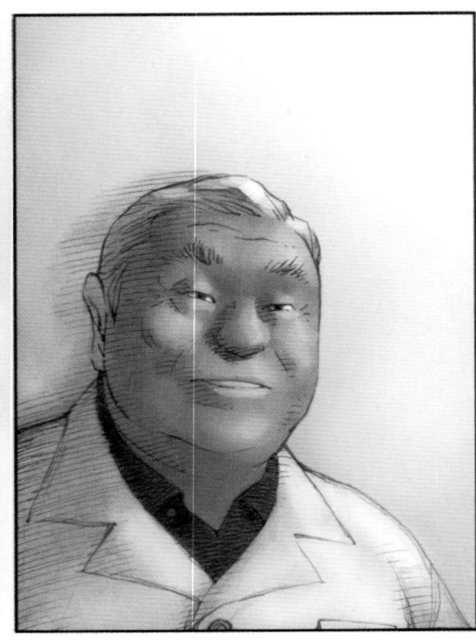

PROBABLY HALF A YEAR.

THEN... I CAN SEE THIS CLASS TO GRADUATION.

I DON'T HAVE ¥20,000.
ANY MONEY I HAVE,
I SPEND ON THE KIDS...
粉面
稀飯
家常小炒

I'VE LOST COUNT OF
HOW MANY STUDENTS
I'VE HELPED.

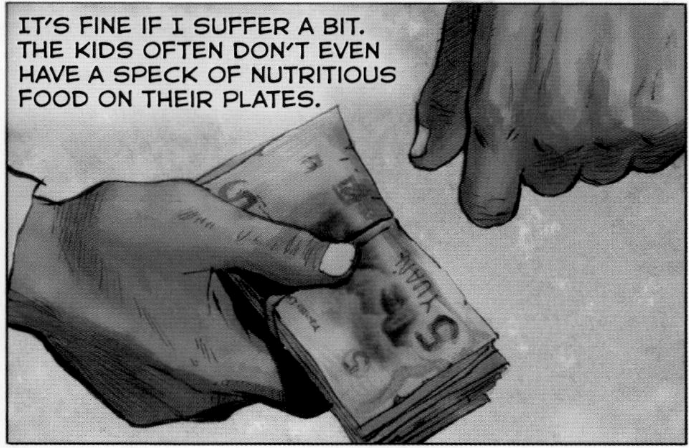
IT'S FINE IF I SUFFER A BIT.
THE KIDS OFTEN DON'T EVEN
HAVE A SPECK OF NUTRITIOUS
FOOD ON THEIR PLATES.

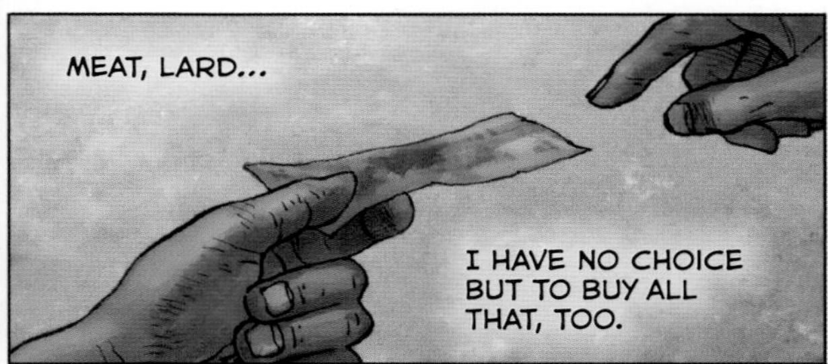
MEAT, LARD...
I HAVE NO CHOICE
BUT TO BUY ALL
THAT, TOO.

I ONLY HAVE A TENTH
OF WHAT I'D NEED
FOR THE SURGERY.

BUT THE CHILDREN HAVE HOPES AND DREAMS, EVEN IN A PLACE AS DESOLATE AS THIS, EVEN WHILE THEY STARE AT THE BLACKBOARD AS THE WIND CHILLS THEM TO THE BONE.

SOME SAY THAT TEACHERS ARE CANDLES. THEY SET THEMSELVES ON FIRE SO THAT OTHERS MAY SEE. HEH...
中外名家
散文

BOSS, GRAB ME ANOTHER ONE OF THOSE *WORLD'S BEST SCIENCE FICTION* ANNUALS.

NO MATTER HOW LONG IT TAKES, NO MATTER HOW DIMLY...
I HAVE TO STAY ALIGHT FROM THE BEGINNING TO THE VERY END.

STAR 1033715... TWO PLANETS DISCOVERED. PLANET 1 SHOWS SIGNS OF LIFE.

PLANET 1

READY
FOR FOUR-
DIMENSIONAL
SCAN.

LIFE FORMS
SECURED.
BEGIN SCAN.

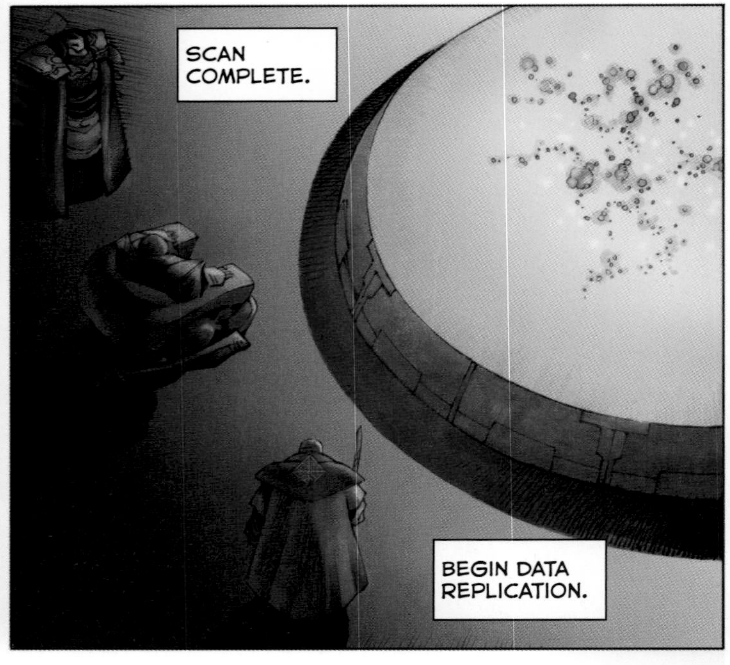
SCAN
COMPLETE.
BEGIN DATA
REPLICATION.

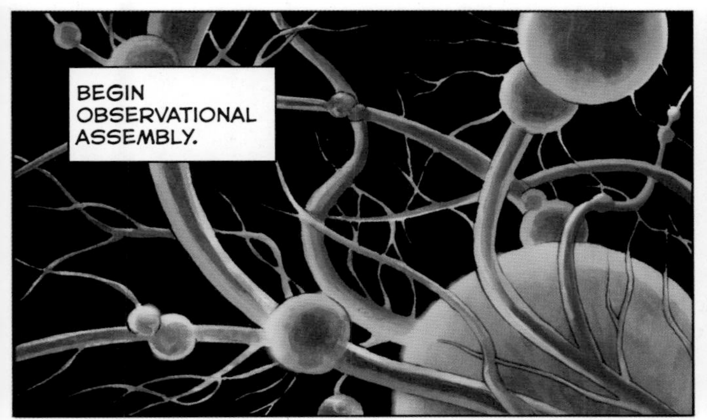
BEGIN OBSERVATIONAL ASSEMBLY.

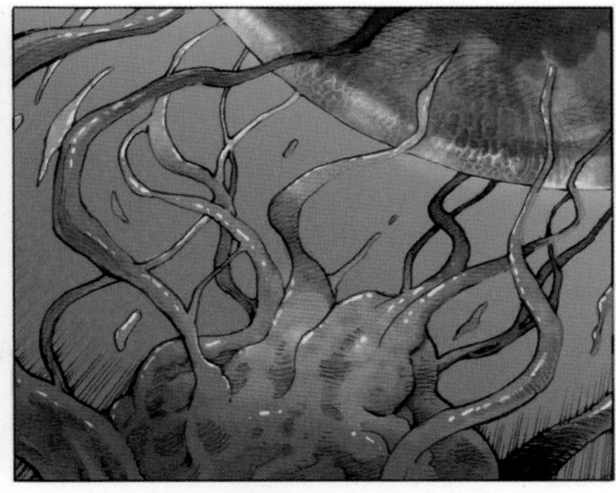

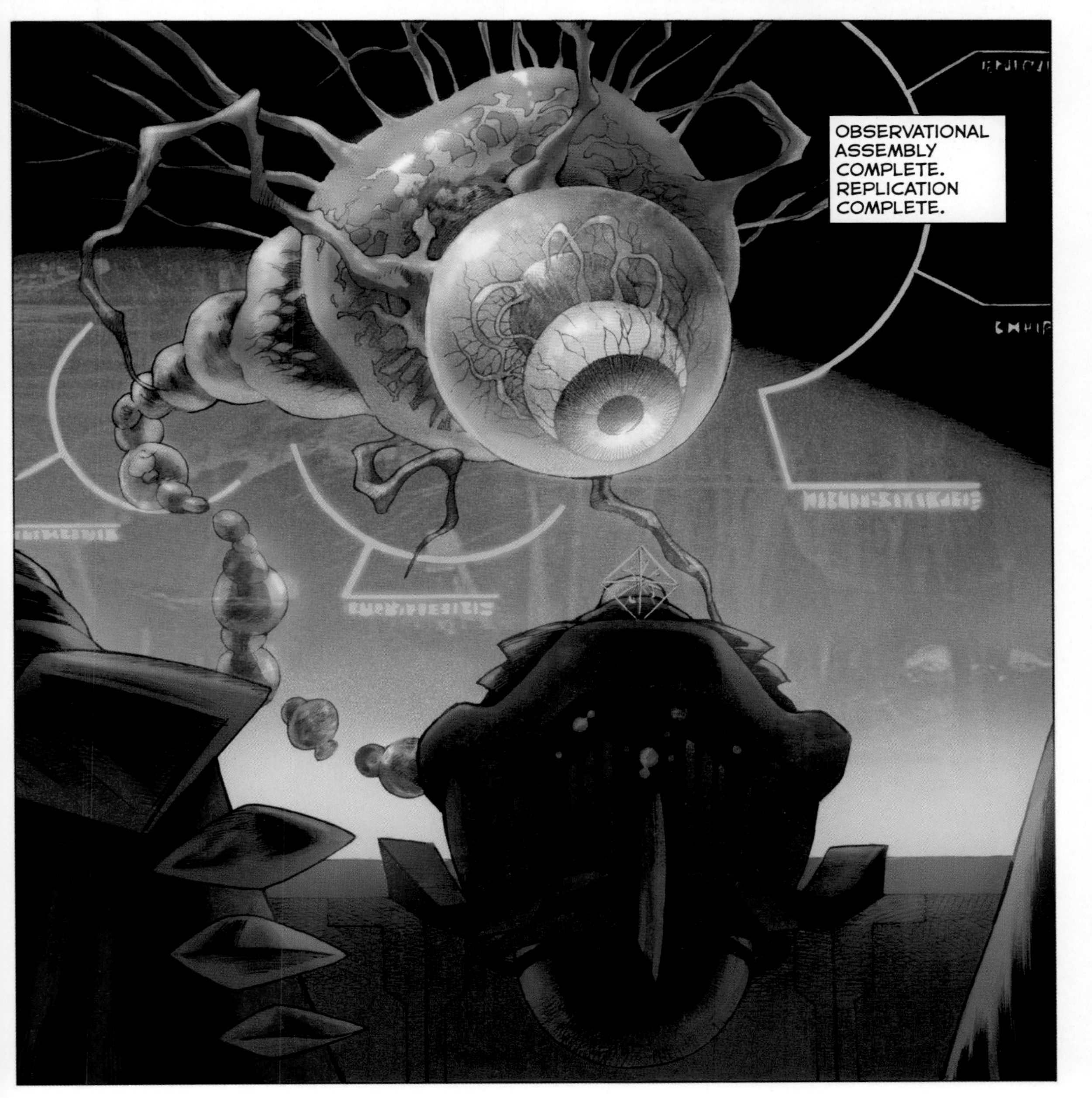
OBSERVATIONAL ASSEMBLY COMPLETE. REPLICATION COMPLETE.

CONSCIOUSNESS CALIBRATED. HIGH-SPEED CONNECTION ESTABLISHED.

BEGIN TESTING FOR LEVEL 3C CIVILIZATION.

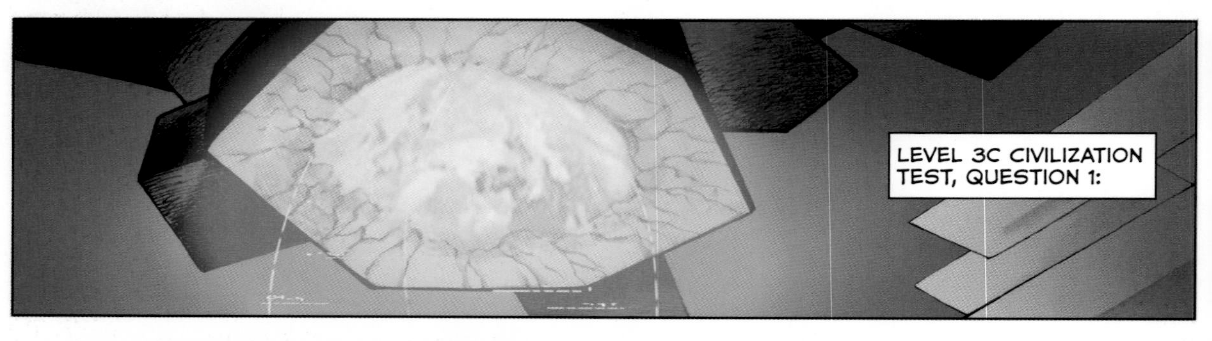
LEVEL 3C CIVILIZATION TEST, QUESTION 1:

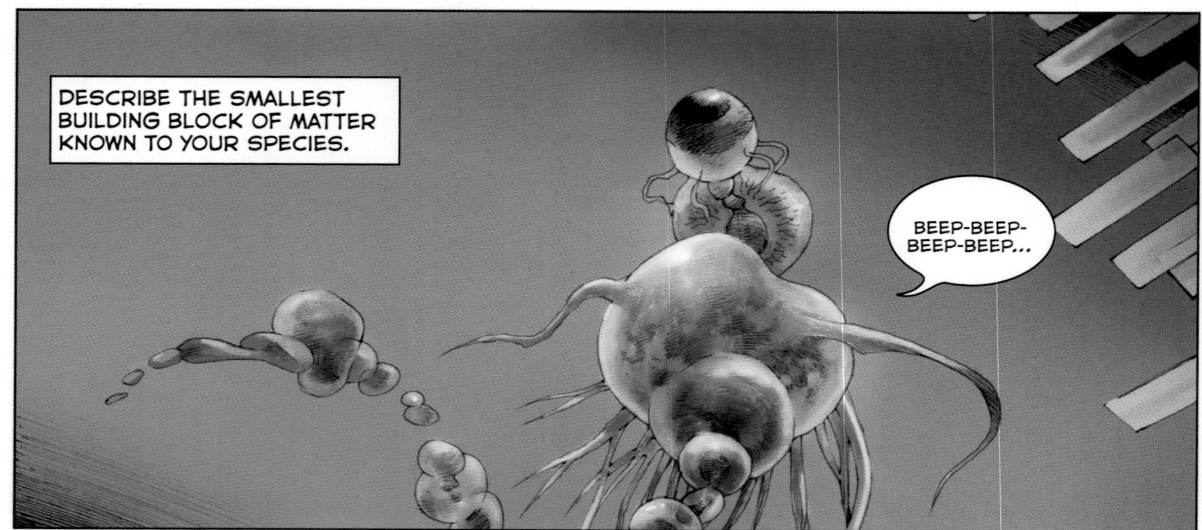
DESCRIBE THE SMALLEST BUILDING BLOCK OF MATTER KNOWN TO YOUR SPECIES.
BEEP-BEEP-BEEP-BEEP...

QUESTION 1
FAILED.
LEVEL 3C CIVILIZATION TEST, QUESTION 2:
WHAT ARE THE CHARACTERIS-TICS OF HEAT? CAN THE FLOW OF ENERGY BE REVERSED?
BEEP-BEEP-BEEP-BEEP...

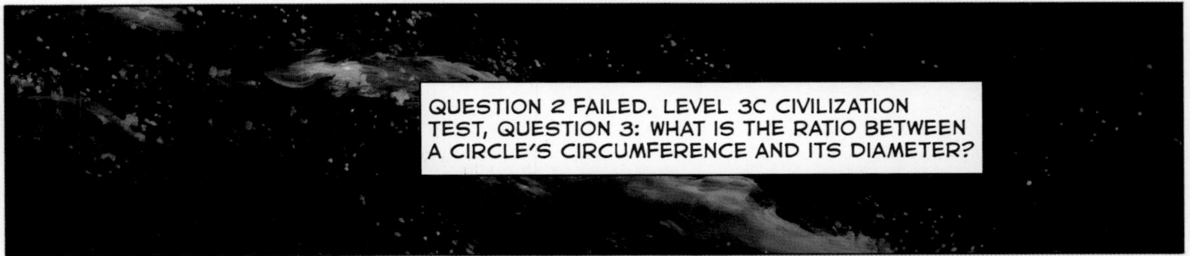
QUESTION 2 FAILED. LEVEL 3C CIVILIZATION TEST, QUESTION 3: WHAT IS THE RATIO BETWEEN A CIRCLE'S CIRCUMFERENCE AND ITS DIAMETER?

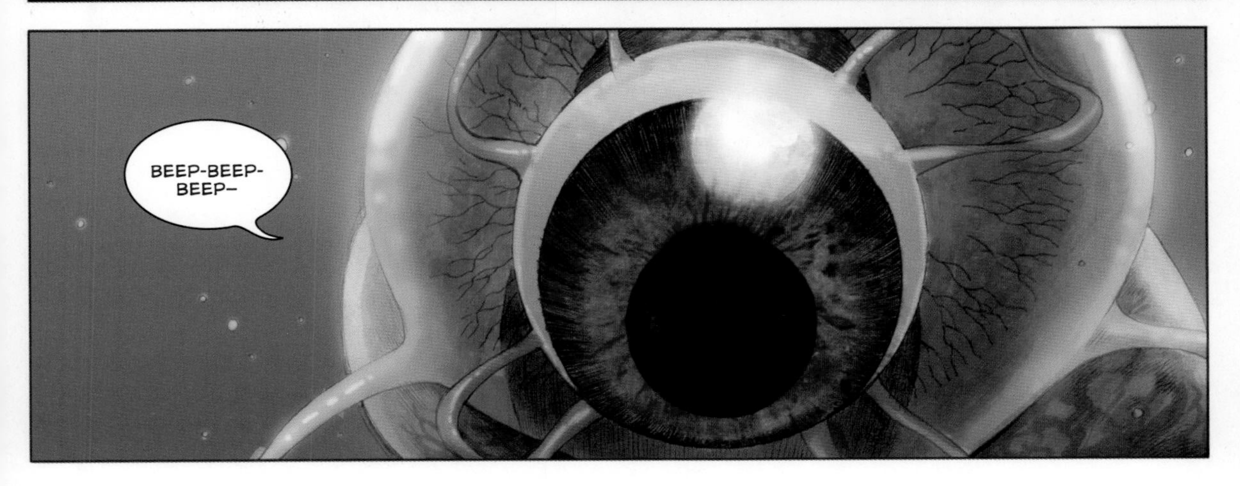
BEEP-BEEP-BEEP–

LET'S STOP HERE. WE DON'T HAVE MUCH TIME.
FIRE THE SINGULARITY MISSILE!
SKREEEEE

COUGH

I DON'T HAVE ANY MORE TIME LEFT.

THE CANCER CELLS SPREAD FASTER THAN EXPECTED.
IT'S ONLY BEEN A COUPLE MONTHS, BUT THE TUMOR HAS ALREADY METASTASIZED TO MY LIVER.

PLEASE, GET SOME REST. YOU CAN CONTINUE TOMORROW...

THAT TIME IS FOR OTHER LESSONS.
I NO LONGER HAVE A TOMORROW.

TODAY, WE'LL DISCUSS NEWTON'S THREE LAWS OF MOTION.

NEWTON WAS A FAMOUS SCIENTIST FROM A PLACE ONCE KNOWN AS ENGLAND. HE DESCRIBED THE THREE RULES THAT ALL MATTER FOLLOWS. NOTHING CAN ESCAPE THE LIMITS SET BY THOSE LAWS: NOT THE SUN, THE MOON, THE SEA OR THE WIND. EVEN DURING A LUNAR ECLIPSE, THE SUN AND MOON STILL FOLLOW THOSE THREE LAWS.

NEWTON'S FIRST LAW: AN OBJECT WILL REMAIN AT REST OR AT A STEADY VELOCITY IN A STRAIGHT LINE UNLESS AN EXTERNAL FORCE ACTS ON IT.

SO, IF YOU PUSH A GRINDSTONE WITH ALL YOUR MIGHT, IT WILL ROLL ON FOREVER AND EVER, NOT EVEN STOPPING AT THE HORIZON...
IMPOSSIBLE, RIGHT? BECAUSE FRICTION EXISTS, SO FRICTION WILL STOP IT EVEN-TUALLY. THERE IS NOWHERE ON THIS PLANET WHERE FRICTION DOESN'T EXIST.

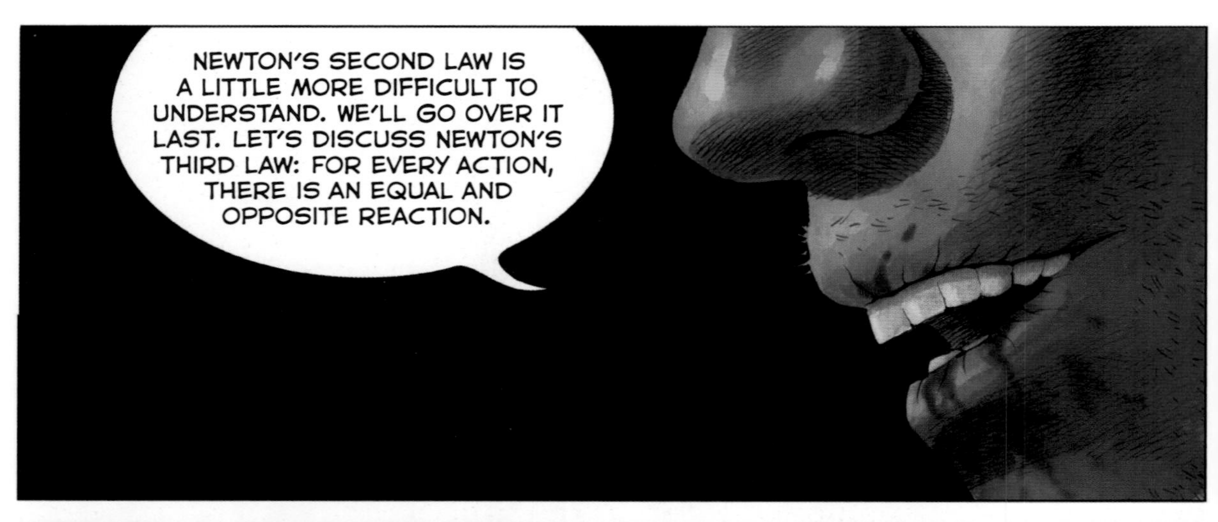
NEWTON'S SECOND LAW IS A LITTLE MORE DIFFICULT TO UNDERSTAND. WE'LL GO OVER IT LAST. LET'S DISCUSS NEWTON'S THIRD LAW: FOR EVERY ACTION, THERE IS AN EQUAL AND OPPOSITE REACTION.

UNDERSTAND? WHO CAN EXPLAIN WHAT THAT MEANS?

THAT DOESN'T MAKE SENSE!
ONE TIME, I WAS FIGHTING WITH LI QUANGUI. HE HIT ME SO HARD, MY WHOLE FACE SWELLED UP. BUT HE DIDN'T HURT HIS HAND AT ALL!
THAT CAN'T BE AN EQUAL POWER—I DEFINITELY GOT THE STRONGER END OF IT!

THAT'S BECAUSE YOUR CHEEK IS SOFTER THAN HIS FIST. BUT THE FORCE THEY APPLY ON EACH OTHER IS STILL THE SAME.
LET'S CONTINUE ON TO NEWTON'S SECOND LAW.

AN OBJECT'S ACCELERATION AND THE FORCE APPLIED TO IT ARE DIRECTLY PROPORTIONAL, WHILE ITS ACCELERATION AND MASS ARE INVERSELY PROPORTIONAL.
ACCELERATION IS THE CHANGE IN VELOCITY AT ANY MOMENT. IT'S NOT THE SAME AS VELOCITY. EVEN AT A HIGH VELOCITY, YOU CAN HAVE LOW ACCELERATION. IF YOU HAVE HIGH ACCELERATION, YOUR VELOCITY MAY STILL BE LOW...
HUFF-PUFF
HUFF-PUFF
UNDER... UNDERSTAND?

WE UNDER-STAND! PLEASE, SIR, TAKE A BREAK!

I KNOW YOU DON'T UNDERSTAND, BUT MEMORIZE IT ANY-WAY, SO YOU CAN MAKE SENSE OF IT LATER. AN OBJECT'S ACCELERATION...

WE GET IT! PLEASE! YOU NEED TO REST!

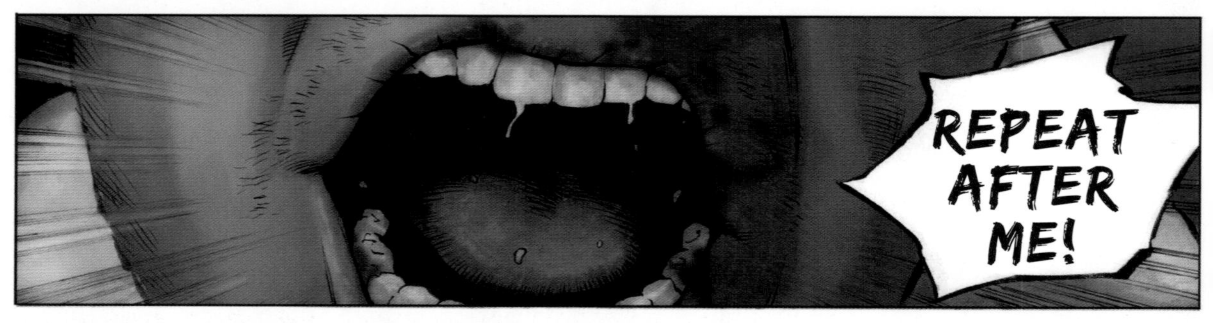
REPEAT AFTER ME!

AN OBJECT'S ACCELERATION AND THE FORCE APPLIED TO IT ARE DIRECTLY PROPORTIONAL, WHILE ITS ACCELERATION AND MASS ARE INVERSELY PROPORTIONAL...

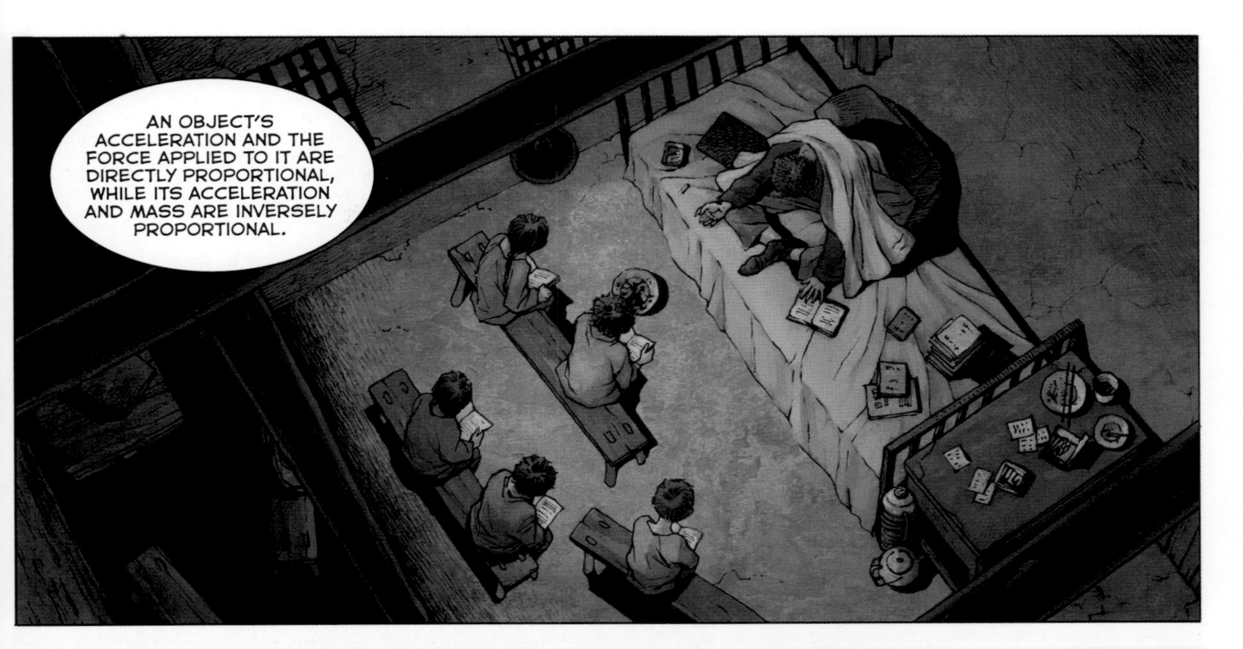
AN OBJECT'S ACCELERATION AND THE FORCE APPLIED TO IT ARE DIRECTLY PROPORTIONAL, WHILE ITS ACCELERATION AND MASS ARE INVERSELY PROPORTIONAL.

AN OBJECT'S ACCELERATION AND THE FORCE APPLIED TO IT ARE DIRECTLY PROPORTIONAL, WHILE ITS ACCELERATION AND MASS ARE INVERSELY PROPORTIONAL.
AN OBJECT'S ACCELERATION AND THE FORCE APPLIED TO IT...

PLANET 1 SAMPLING RESULTS...
GREEN! GREEN! BLUE 84210
REPORTING.

LIFE FOUND ON
PLANET 3 OF STAR
500921473!

LIFE FORMS SECURED...
BEGINNING SCAN FOR CONSCIOUSNESS...
BEGINNING DATA REPLICATION...
INITIALIZING OBSERVATIONAL ASSEMBLY...

OBSERVATIONAL ASSEMBLY COMPLETE.

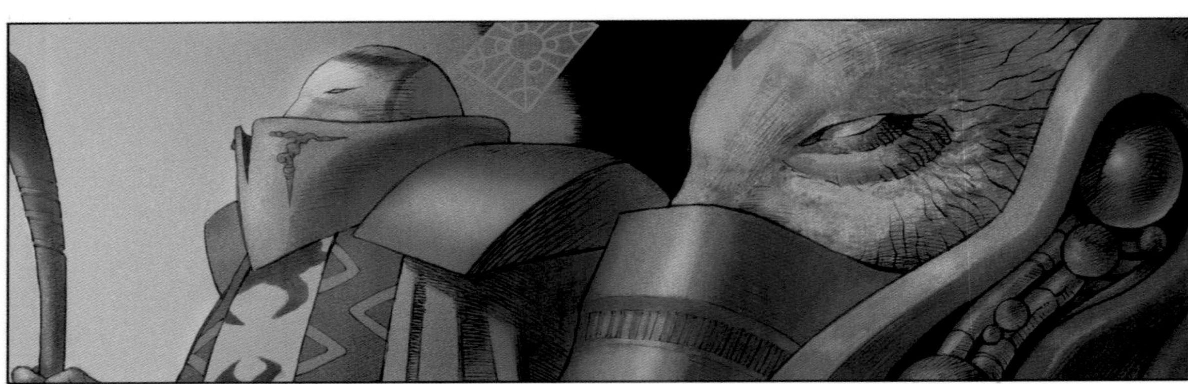

BEGIN TESTING
FOR LEVEL 3C
CIVILIZATION.

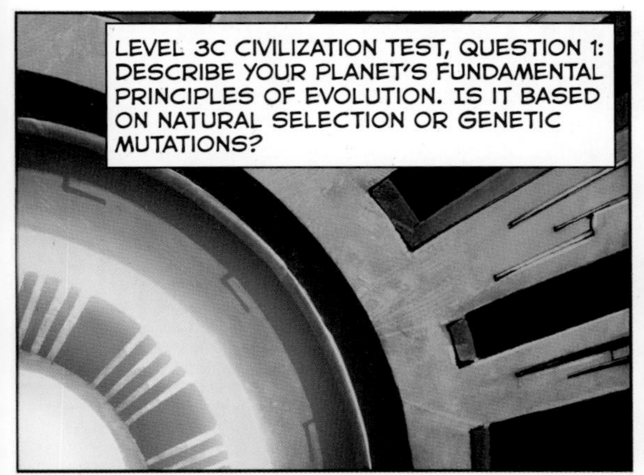
LEVEL 3C CIVILIZATION TEST, QUESTION 1: DESCRIBE YOUR PLANET'S FUNDAMENTAL PRINCIPLES OF EVOLUTION. IS IT BASED ON NATURAL SELECTION OR GENETIC MUTATIONS?

...

LEVEL 3C CIVILIZATION TEST, QUESTION 2: WHAT IS A STAR'S ENERGY SOURCE?
...

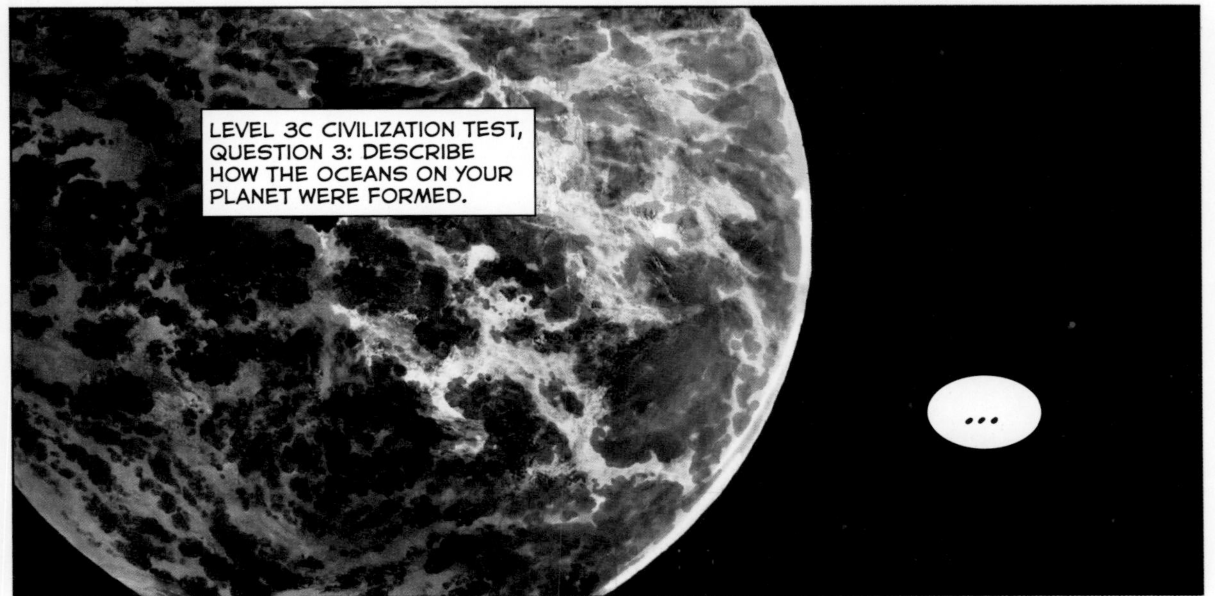
LEVEL 3C CIVILIZATION TEST, QUESTION 3: DESCRIBE HOW THE OCEANS ON YOUR PLANET WERE FORMED.
...

THE LIFE HERE IS FAR TOO LOW-LEVEL... EVEN IF THERE *ARE* SIGNS OF INTELLIGENCE, THEY HAVEN'T YET REACHED CIVILIZATION.
FIRE THE SINGULARITY MISSILE!
SKREEEEEE

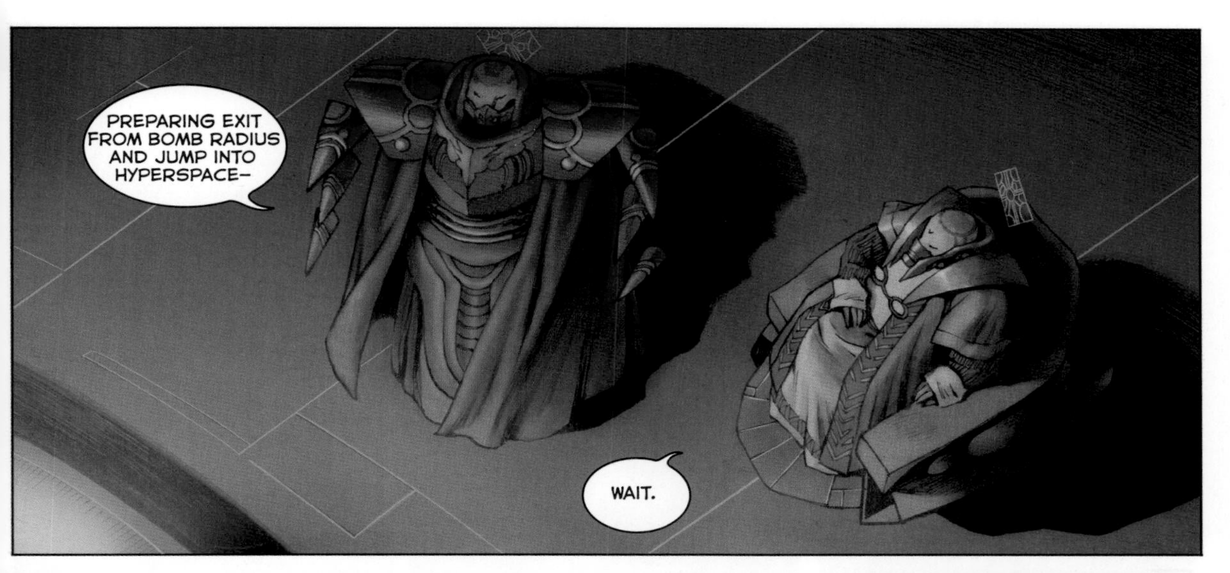
PREPARING EXIT FROM BOMB RADIUS AND JUMP INTO HYPERSPACE–
WAIT.

HOW MUCH LONGER UNTIL THE MISSILE REACHES ITS DESTINATION?
ABOUT TEN MINUTES.

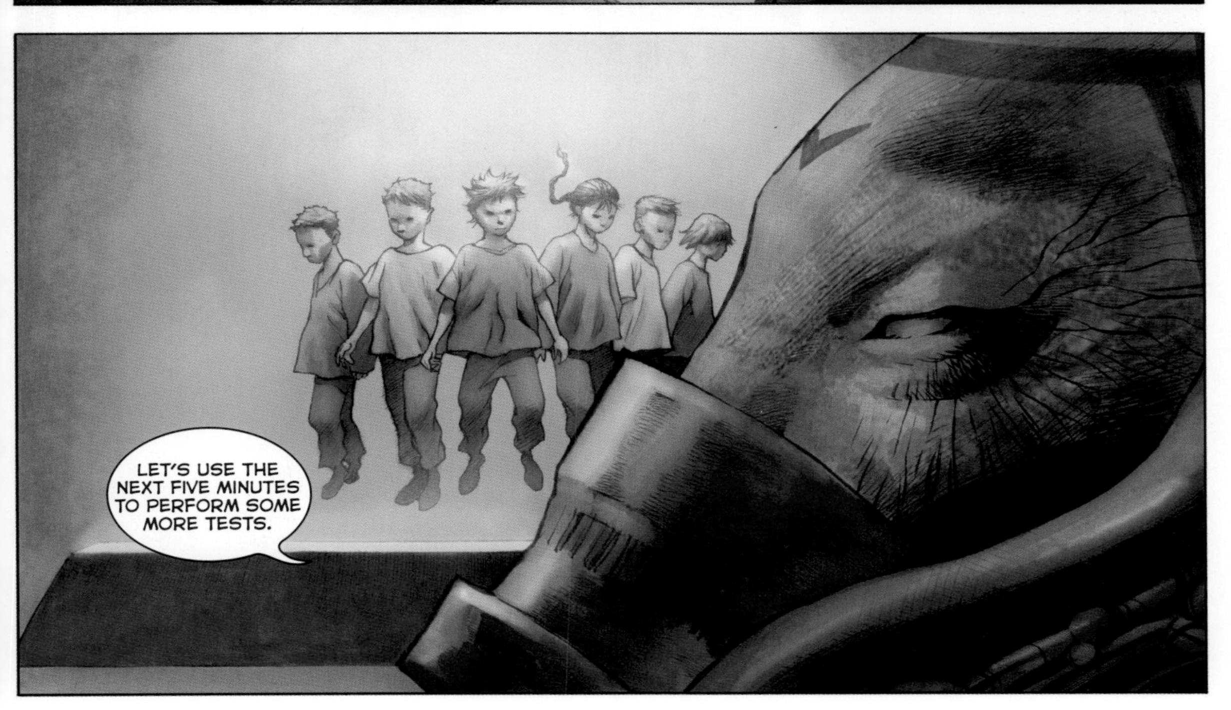
LET'S USE THE NEXT FIVE MINUTES TO PERFORM SOME MORE TESTS.

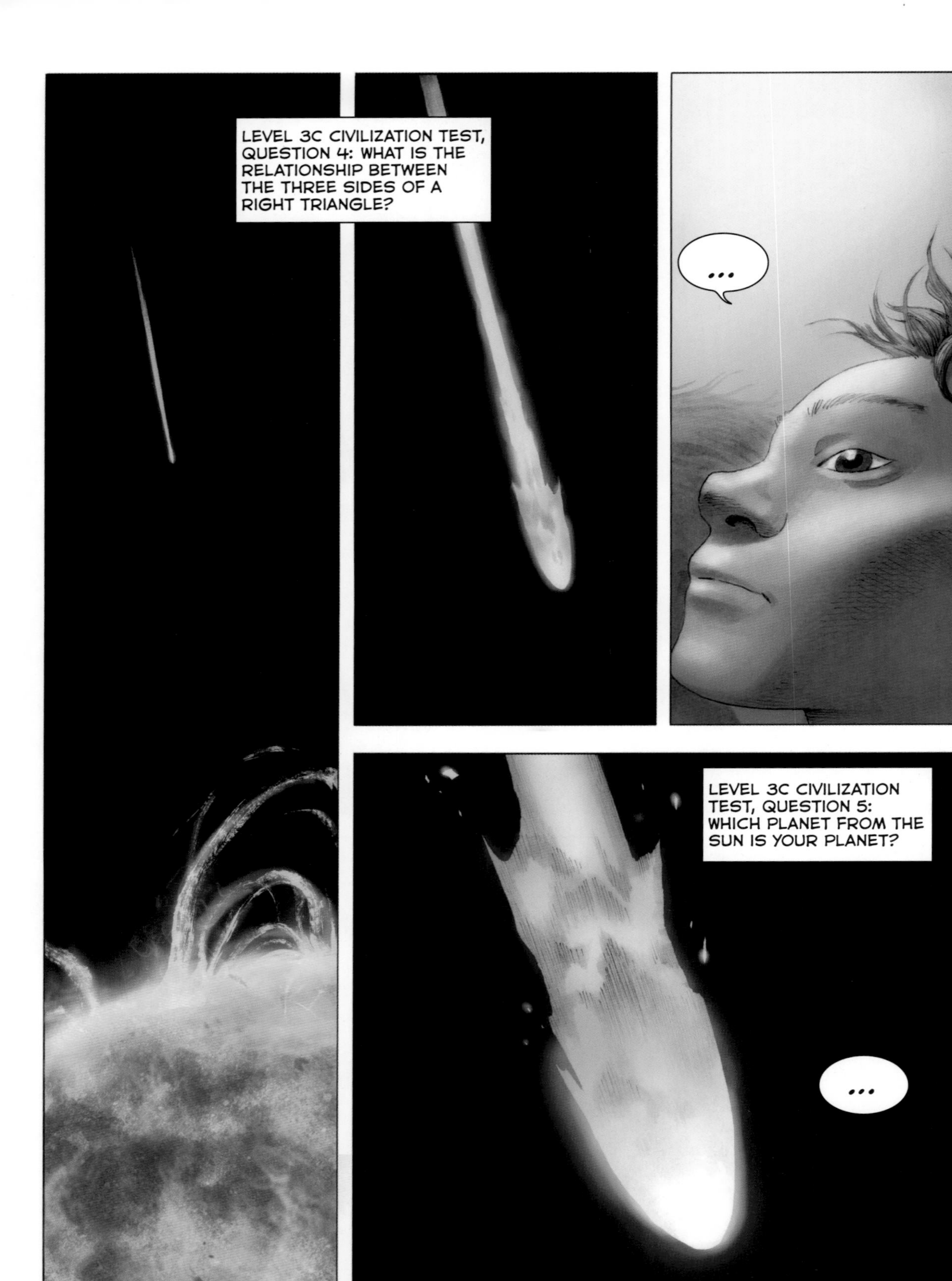
LEVEL 3C CIVILIZATION TEST, QUESTION 4: WHAT IS THE RELATIONSHIP BETWEEN THE THREE SIDES OF A RIGHT TRIANGLE?
...
LEVEL 3C CIVILIZATION TEST, QUESTION 5: WHICH PLANET FROM THE SUN IS YOUR PLANET?
...

LEVEL 3C CIVILIZATION TEST, QUESTION 6...
...

IT'S NO USE, SIR.

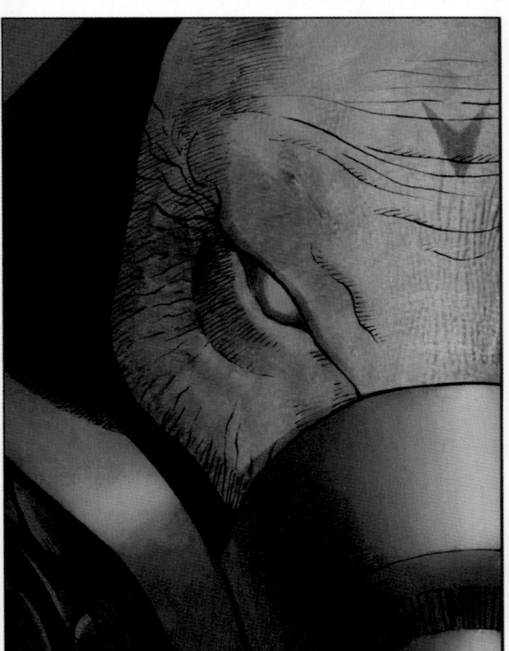

LEVEL 3C CIVILIZATION TEST, QUESTION 7...
...

LEVEL 3C CIVILIZATION TEST, QUESTION 8: WHAT IS AN OBJECT'S STATE BEFORE AN EXTERNAL FORCE ACTS ON IT?

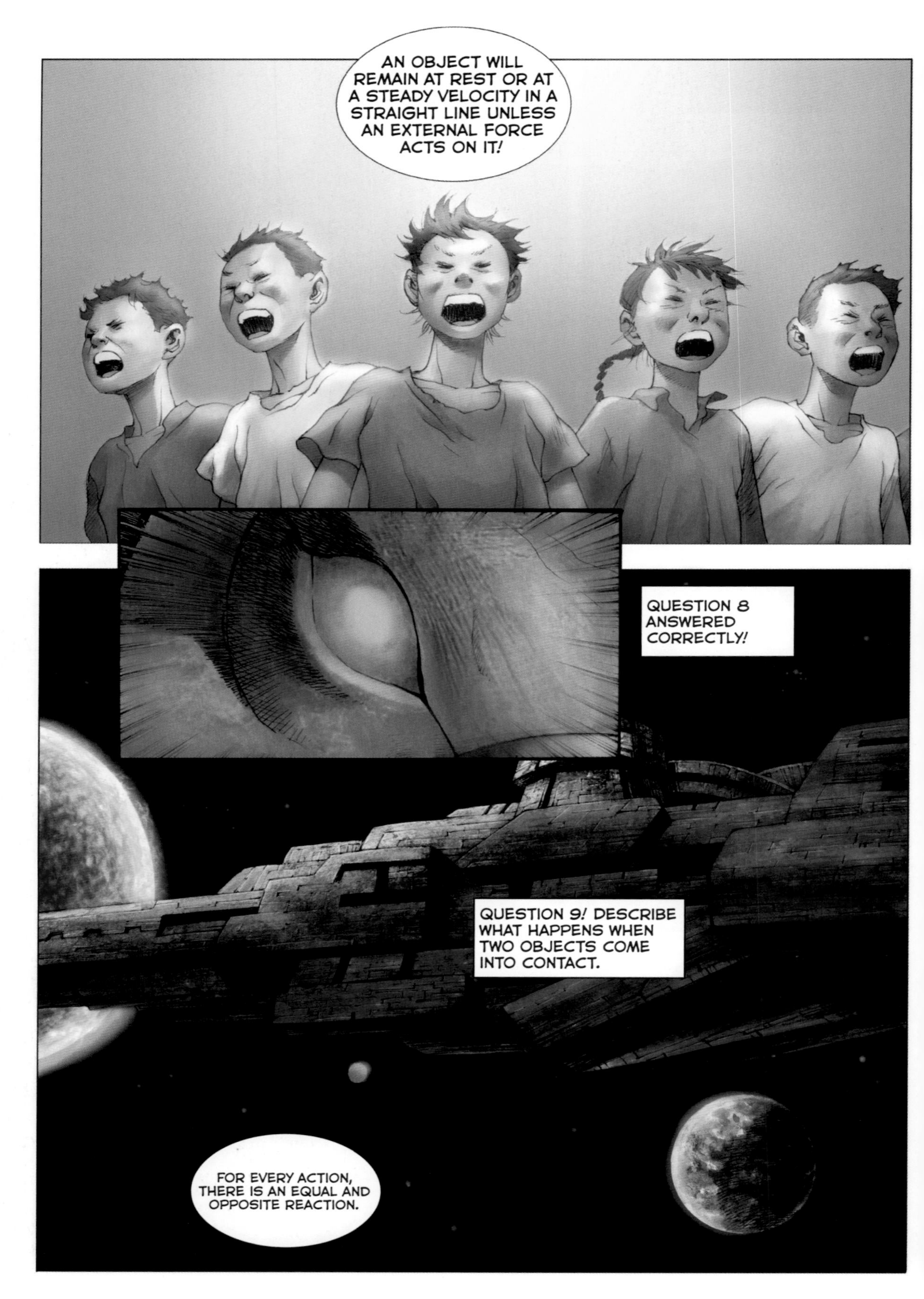
AN OBJECT WILL REMAIN AT REST OR AT A STEADY VELOCITY IN A STRAIGHT LINE UNLESS AN EXTERNAL FORCE ACTS ON IT!
QUESTION 8 ANSWERED CORRECTLY!
QUESTION 9! DESCRIBE WHAT HAPPENS WHEN TWO OBJECTS COME INTO CONTACT.
FOR EVERY ACTION, THERE IS AN EQUAL AND OPPOSITE REACTION.

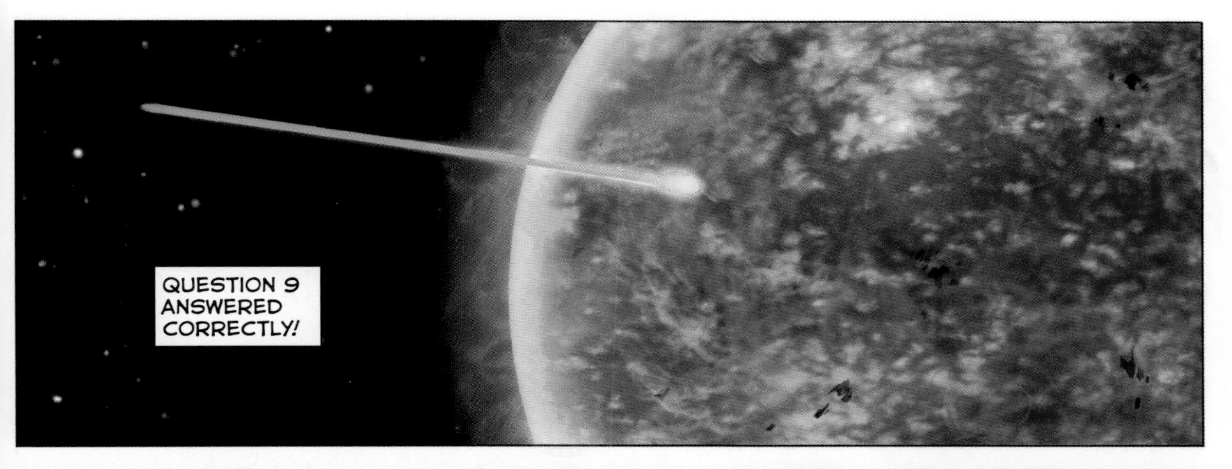
QUESTION 9
ANSWERED
CORRECTLY!

QUESTION 10: DESCRIBE THE RELATIONSHIP BETWEEN AN OBJECT'S MASS, FORCE, AND ACCELERATION.

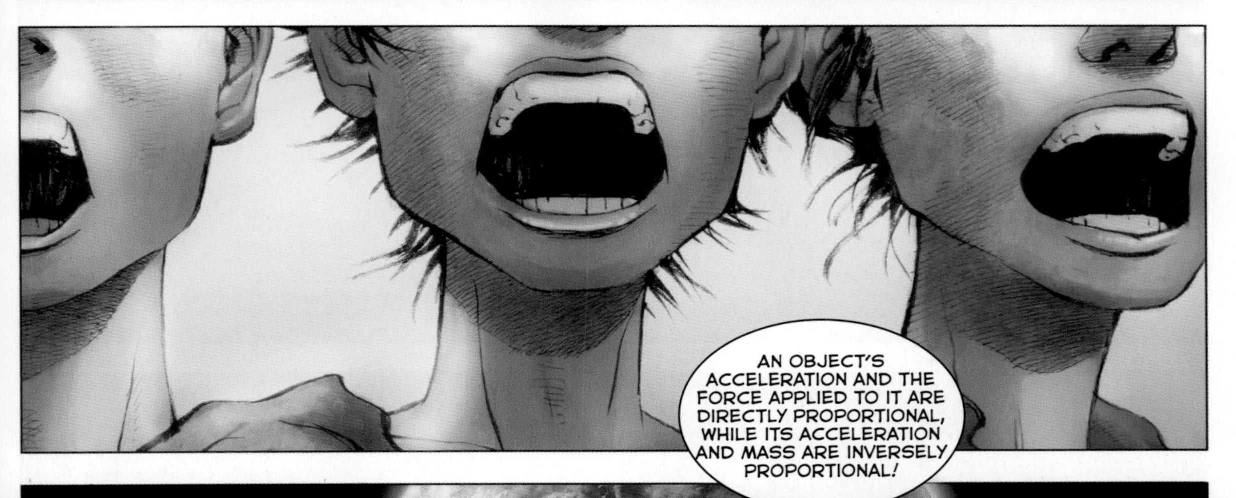
AN OBJECT'S ACCELERATION AND THE FORCE APPLIED TO IT ARE DIRECTLY PROPORTIONAL, WHILE ITS ACCELERATION AND MASS ARE INVERSELY PROPORTIONAL!

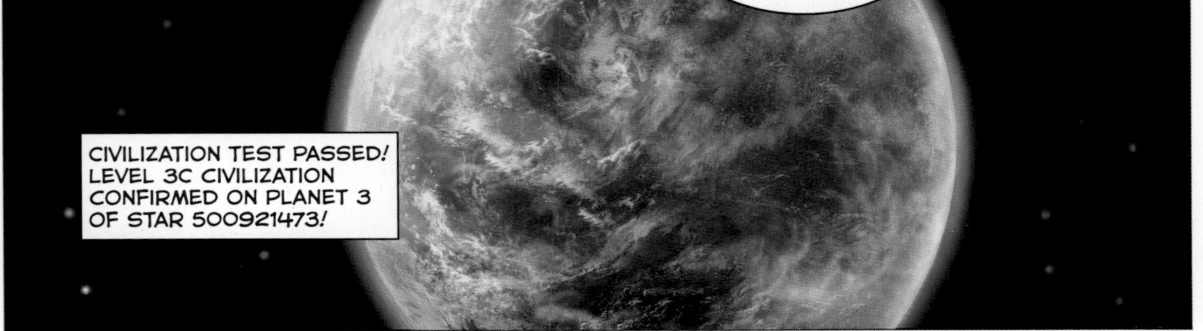
CIVILIZATION TEST PASSED! LEVEL 3C CIVILIZATION CONFIRMED ON PLANET 3 OF STAR 500921473!

REROUTE THE MISSILE!

FORCE FIELDS AT MAXIMUM POWER. ADJUSTING COURSE!

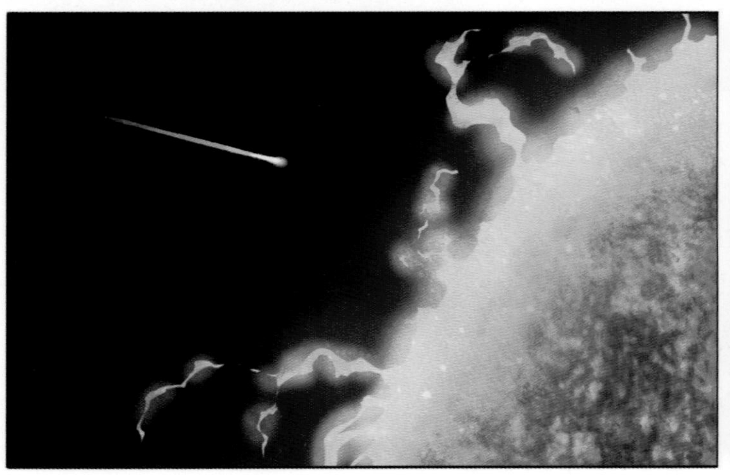

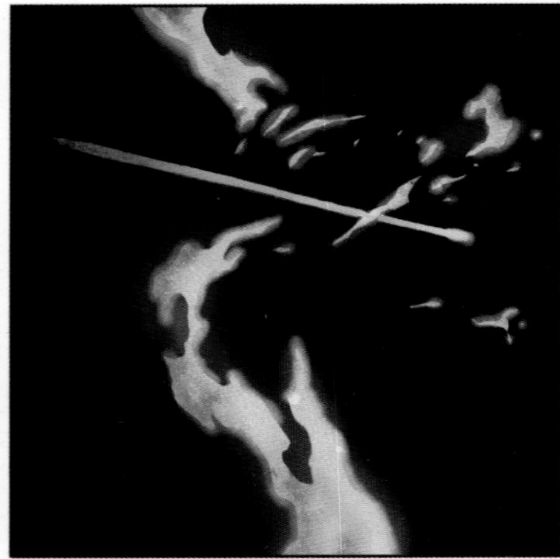

WE NEARLY DESTROYED A CARBON CIVILIZATION...
UNBELIEVABLE— THERE'S LEVEL 3C CIVILIZATION EVEN IN A PLACE AS REMOTE AS THIS!
OF COURSE. WHETHER THE CARBONWEALTH OR THE SILICON EMPIRE, LIFE ISN'T CONFINED TO JUST ONE PART OF THE UNIVERSE. BUT IT'S QUITE UNUSUAL FOR A CIVILIZATION TO REACH THAT LEVEL OF COMPLEXITY BY ITSELF.

LEAVE ONE OF THE VESSELS HERE TO CONTINUE TESTING.

SOB
MR. LI... SOB
SHOULDN'T WE TELL THE ADULTS?

WHAT USE WOULD THAT BE? NO ONE LIKED HIM WHEN HE WAS *ALIVE*. THEY WON'T SPARE A CENT FOR A COFFIN.
WE DON'T NEED HELP! HE'S *OUR* TEACHER. *WE'LL* BURY HIM!

李老师之墓

THE RESULTS OF THE LAST ROUND OF TESTING ARE IN. THIS PLANET DOESN'T HAVE LEVEL 3C CIVILIZATION...

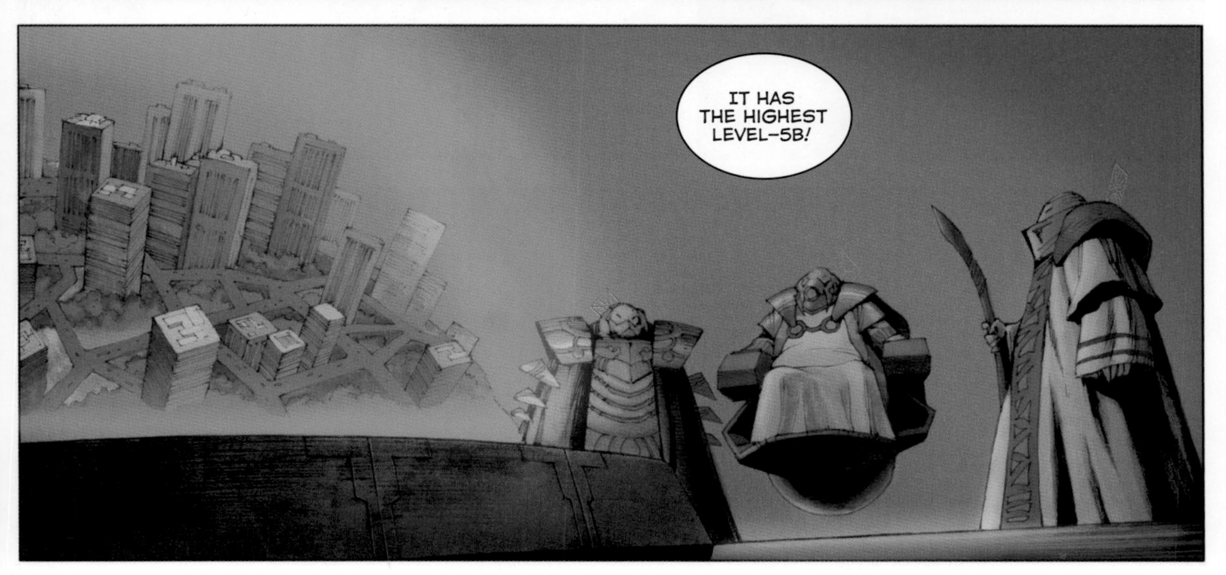
IT HAS THE HIGHEST LEVEL-5B!

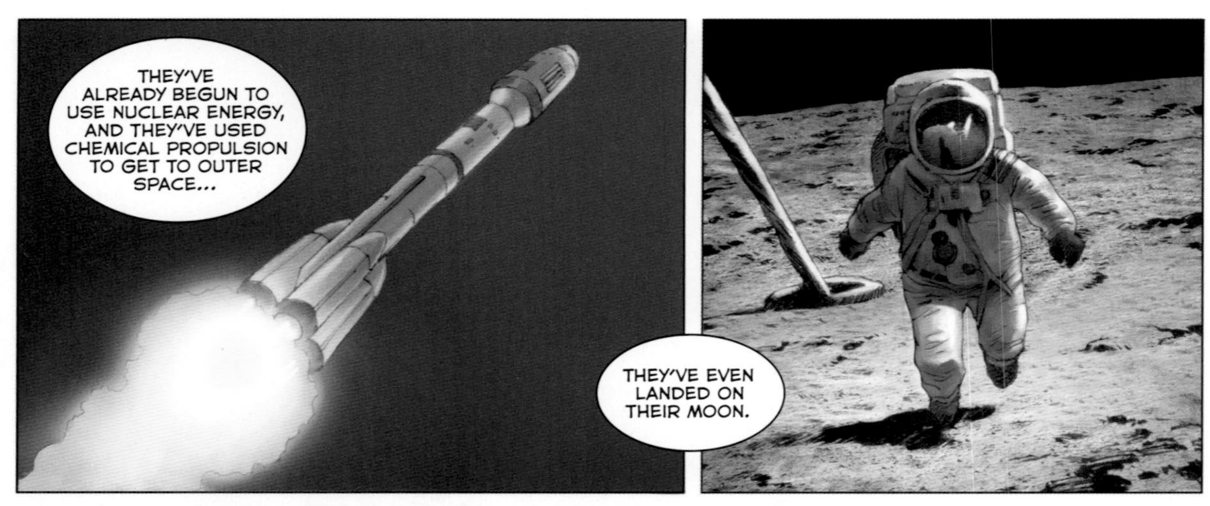
THEY'VE ALREADY BEGUN TO USE NUCLEAR ENERGY, AND THEY'VE USED CHEMICAL PROPULSION TO GET TO OUTER SPACE...
THEY'VE EVEN LANDED ON THEIR MOON.

HOW GOOD ARE THESE LIFE FORMS AT TRANSFERRING MEMORIES?
THEY CAN'T TRANSFER MEMORIES. THEY ACQUIRE ALL MEMORIES AFTER BIRTH.

THEN HOW DO THEY COMMUNICATE WITH EACH OTHER?

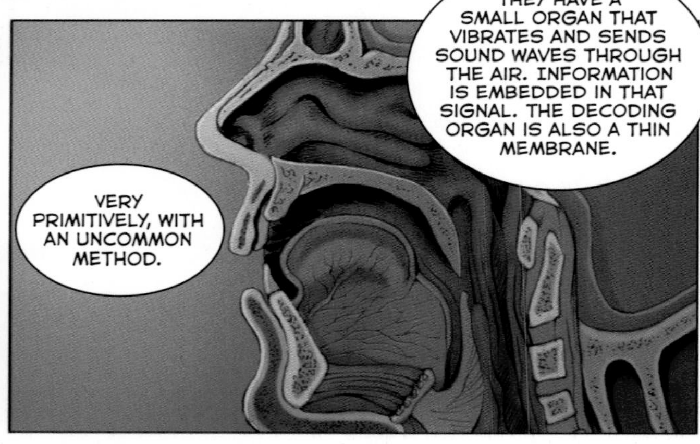
VERY PRIMITIVELY, WITH AN UNCOMMON METHOD.
THEY HAVE A SMALL ORGAN THAT VIBRATES AND SENDS SOUND WAVES THROUGH THE AIR. INFORMATION IS EMBEDDED IN THAT SIGNAL. THE DECODING ORGAN IS ALSO A THIN MEMBRANE.

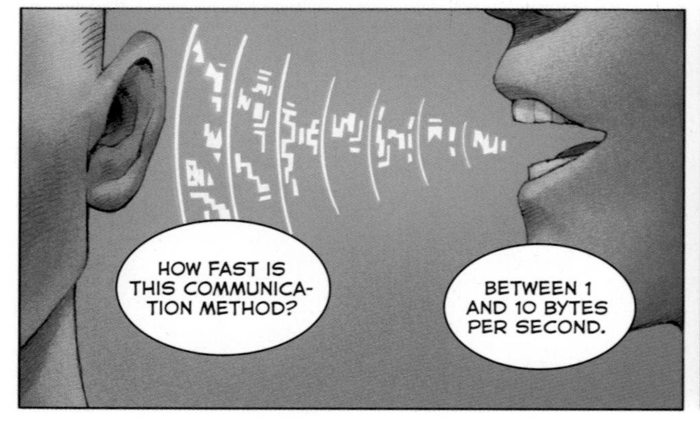
HOW FAST IS THIS COMMUNICATION METHOD?
BETWEEN 1 AND 10 BYTES PER SECOND.

WHAT?!

SIR, HAVE YOU LOST YOUR MIND? CAN A SPECIES THAT CAN'T TRANSFER MEMORIES AND THAT USES AN AUDIO SIGNAL WITH A SPEED OF *ONE BYTE PER SECOND* TRULY CREATE A LEVEL 5B CIVILIZATION?
WITHOUT OUTSIDE HELP? THIS AROSE SPONTANEOUSLY?!

IT SEEMS TO BE THAT WAY, SIR. WE DIDN'T BELIEVE IT AT FIRST EITHER, BUT WE VERIFIED THE RESULTS MULTIPLE TIMES.

UNDER THOSE CONDITIONS, A SPECIES CAN'T POSSIBLY PASS EVERYTHING LEARNED BY ONE GENERATION DOWN TO THE NEXT—WHICH YOU NEED TO BE ABLE TO DO TO CREATE A CIVILIZATION!

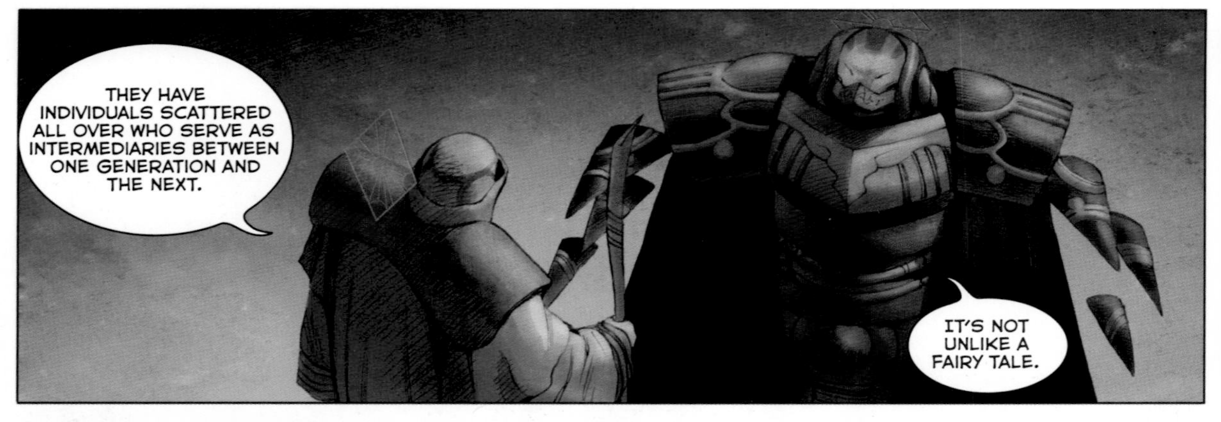
THEY HAVE INDIVIDUALS SCATTERED ALL OVER WHO SERVE AS INTERMEDIARIES BETWEEN ONE GENERATION AND THE NEXT.
IT'S NOT UNLIKE A FAIRY TALE.

NO...

ONCE UPON A TIME IN THE MILKY WAY, THERE WAS SUCH A THING...

BUT EVEN THEN, THEY WERE RARE. OTHER THAN THOSE OF US WHO STUDY THE EVOLUTIONARY HISTORY OF GALACTIC CIVILIZATIONS, VERY FEW PEOPLE KNOW ABOUT THEM...

THERE'S AN ANCIENT WORD FOR THE PEOPLE IN CHARGE OF PASSING ON KNOWLEDGE BETWEEN GENERATIONS. IT'S NEARLY BEEN FORGOTTEN– MANY HISTORICAL LINGUISTIC DATABASES DON'T EVEN HAVE AN ENTRY FOR IT.

THEY WERE CALLED–

TEACHERS.

CIXIN LIU is China's #1 SF writer and author of *The Three-Body Problem* – the first-ever translated novel to win a Hugo Award. Prior to becoming a writer, Liu worked as an engineer in a power plant in Yangquan.

ZHANG XIAOYU is a Chinese graphic novel artist. He is one of few Chinese graphic novel artists to have achieved international influence, and has served a great contribution to revitalising the form in China and disseminating Chinese culture in the wider world. His work has been recognised with prizes both within China and internationally.

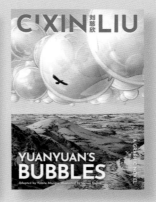